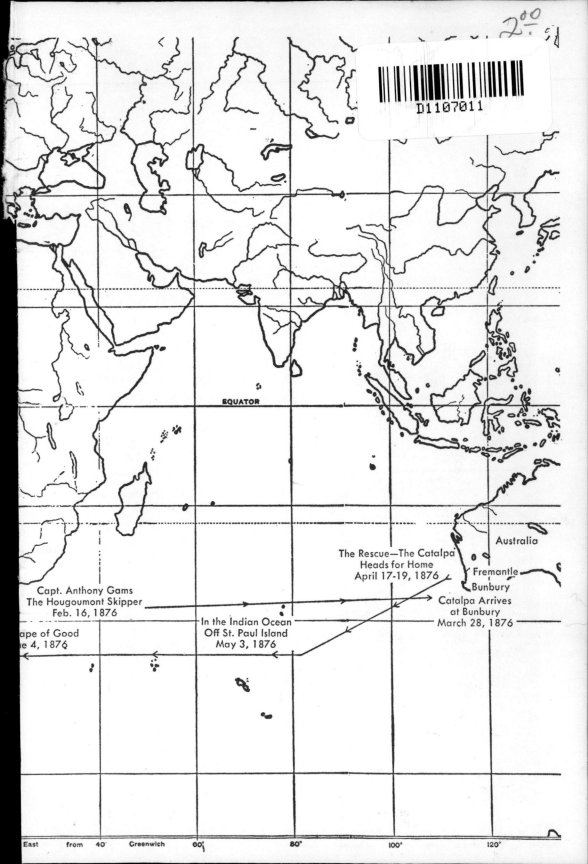

EQUATOR

The Rescue—The Catalpa
Heads for Home
April 17-19, 1876

Australia

Fremantle

Bunbury

Capt. Anthony Gams
The Hougoumont Skipper
Feb. 16, 1876

Catalpa Arrives
at Bunbury
March 28, 1876

In the Indian Ocean
Off St. Paul Island
May 3, 1876

ape of Good
e 4, 1876

East   from   40°   Greenwich   60°   80°   100°   120°

The
Emerald
Whaler

The Emerald Whaler

By William J. Laubenstein

THE **BOBBS-MERRILL** COMPANY, INC.
A SUBSIDIARY OF HOWARD W. SAMS & CO., INC.
Publishers • INDIANAPOLIS • NEW YORK

To all those lovers of Freedom
to whom the Emerald of Ireland
is the fairest color on
God's Earth . . . and
to the humble, trusting,
patriotic rank and file of
a great secret organization
who, out of small earnings,
contributed regularly and
generously to the fund that made
the *Catalpa* expedition possible,
meanwhile keeping their own
counsel and asking no questions.

"We will make war upon them to death
to recover the independence which is
our natural right; being compelled there-
to by very necessity, and willing rather
to brave danger like men, than to lan-
guish under insult."
—Donal O'Neill, Prince of Ulster

Foreword

In 1865 Irish patriots waited for word, as they had so many times in the past, to rise and throw off English shackles.

Since 1171, when Henry II landed in Waterford, the Irish people had fought for freedom desperately, bitterly, but never hopelessly. They had suffered the terrible anti-Catholic hatred of licentious Henry VIII, the merciless wrath of Queen Elizabeth I, the godless massacres of Oliver Cromwell, the frightful Penal Laws which forced school and Church underground, the infamous Union with England. The Irish people, decimated by the sword, were nearly destroyed by the catastrophic calamity of the Famine of 1847-48. It was then *The London Times* gloated: "They are going! They are going! The Irish are going with a vengeance! Soon a Celt will be as rare in Ireland as a red Indian on the shores of Manhattan!"

But always the Irish had hope. They had hope in the days of the great Connor of Maenmagh, of Shane O'Neill, of Theobald Wolfe Tone, of Robert Emmet, of Dan O'Connell.

And, in 1858 the Irish gained hope anew in James Stephens and the Fenians.

Stephens had a bold plan for his "Rising." He would organize not only the citizens—in Carlow and Wicklow, in Kildare and Athy, in Nass and Meath, in Longford, Wexford, Kilkenny, Cork, Limerick, Mayo, Tipperary, Clare, Galway, Sligo—he would recruit to the Fenian cause Irish sympathizers in Queen Victoria's armed forces in Ireland. He would smuggle guns from America. He would hire American Union Army officers to lead his army.

Organize he did to the extent of three quarters of the Queen's armies in Ireland and thousands upon thousands of citizens. Guns he procured. American officers he hired. But, fatally, Stephens waited. With the best conspiracy ever in Irish revolutionary history, he did not give the word. His "Rising" collapsed. Thousands were arrested, imprisoned, exiled.

But out of the disaster of the Rising of 1865 came one of the greatest rescue stories of all time—the story of the *Catalpa* expedition.

I have had the help and guidance of many kind and co-operative people in searching out the facts about the *Catalpa* adventure. There is room here to mention only a few, such as:

Mr. Arthur Hand, of Roslindale, Massachusetts, a Clan-na-Gael stalwart and long-time friend of Henry Hathaway, with whom the project was first discussed and whose help in correction and revision has been invaluable. He it was who introduced me to many other Irish patriots, all of whom were enthusiastic about the plan for the book.

Mr. James Reidy, of Brooklyn, New York, who was right-hand man to John Devoy in editing *The Gaelic American*. Mr. Reidy gave up his own newspaper in New Rochelle, New York, in 1903 to join Mr. Devoy on that crusading Irish-American newspaper. He helped Mr. Devoy decode the message from Ireland revealing the date of the Easter Rising in 1916.

The untimely death of Mr. Reidy brought me into close contact with his two daughters, Miss Nona Reidy and Miss Ethna Reidy, who as tiny girls recall sitting on the lap of John Devoy. They graciously and unceasingly searched through their father's valuable papers, unearthing many new facts about the *Catalpa* venture, and then permitted me to examine the files of *The Gaelic American*.

No story that involves whaling in the days of wooden ships could be written without the aid of Mr. William E. Tripp, curator-emeritus of the Old Dartmouth Historical Society and Whaling Museum on Johnny Cake Hill in the old-time whaling capital of New Bedford. Mr. Tripp was patient and painstaking in his efforts to provide authentic information about whaling in general, and the voyage of the *Catalpa* in particular. He provided the opportunity for an unhurried reading of the *Catalpa's* log and helped, with his charts, to fix her position at various times during the voyage.

For life aboard a whaler there could be no greater authority than Mr. Reginald Hegarty of New Bedford, a member of the Whaling Museum staff. He went whaling for the first time as a baby of twenty months. By the time he was twelve years old he had completed a four-year voyage on the *Alice Knowles*, with his father as captain. The *Alice Knowles* holds the world's record for oil taken in the shortest space of time, set another world's record for cutting-in six whales in a single day, and at one time had whales alongside for sixty consecutive days. Mr. Hegarty's immense fund of lore about the ways of a whaler, unfolded as we sat on the deck of the Museum's half-size model whaleship, the *Lagoda*, was invaluable.

Authentic information about Captain George Smith Anthony, his wife, his children, his home and his father-in-law, John Richardson, came from Leon M. Huggins, Captain Anthony's son-in-law, of New Bedford.

From Father P. McCarthy, O.M.I., research grantee (postgraduate), University of Western Australia, came most helpful facts about Father Patrick McCabe.

Gordon C. Avery, of the Morse Twist Drill Works, New Bedford, gave information relating to Captain Anthony's work there.

The Reverend Charles Thurber, of the Mariner's Home and Seamen's Bethel, on Johnny Cake Hill, New Bedford, was particularly helpful with his tales of whaling and whalemen.

Authentic details about the convict ship *Hougoumont* came from co-operative gentlemen of the staff of the National Maritime Museum, Greenwich, S.E. 10, London.

My special thanks go to Mr. Peter Conroy, of Boston, for his kindness in lending me his own prized copy of John Devoy's book *Recollections of an Irish Rebel*.

I wish also to acknowledge the assistance and co-operation of Mr. C. Russell Mason and Miss Ruth Emory, of the Massachusetts

Audubon Society; the Very Reverend J. J. Rafferty, Chancellor, Archdiocese of Perth, Western Australia; the Reverend John E. Murphy, S.J., Boston College; Miss Mollie Lukis, Librarian, Battye Library of West Australia History, Perth; and the British Information Service, New York.

And thanks to the enthusiastic staff of the Mystic Seaport and Maritime Historical Museum at Mystic, Connecticut, where I spent many hours prowling around the last and greatest of New Bedford's whalers—the *Charles W. Morgan*, now permanently enshrined at her dock in the re-created New England seaport village there.

Finally, thanks to Miss Sally Johnson for her extremely helpful suggestions, her patience, and her enthusiasm for the whole story of the *Catalpa*.

WILLIAM J. LAUBENSTEIN

- Contents

The
Emerald
Whaler

1 . Last Act of a Tragedy

A biting wind swept slashing rain from the English Channel across Chesil Bank and all the four-and-a-half-mile length of Portland Bill, whipping the harbor into a lather of whitecaps, roaring through the rigging of the ships that cowered behind the new mole, and sending the sea pounding against the stone quays where the town of Portland began. Behind the limestone walls of her Majesty Queen Victoria's Royal prison only the monotonous tread of the warders and the sleep-noises of a thousand-odd prisoners stirred the silence of the dim corridors whose walls dripped water like a sour kitchen sponge. There England's unwanted huddled on planks under thin cotton covers—and the oppressive blanket of dread.

In this reeking catch-all special guards paced before seven doubly locked and barred cells, in which languished seven men with their legs in iron fetters. Each was classified as dangerous in the extreme not only to Queen Victoria's government, but to Her Most Gracious Majesty herself.

That these seven were alive was not due to any mercy on the part of Queen Victoria, nor any twinge of conscience on the part of here ailing Prime Minister, Edward George Geoffrey Smith, 14th Earl of Derby. Rather it was due to a surge of indignation from civilized people of the globe aroused at last to realization of the plight of tortured Ireland.

The English press had pilloried these seven as traitors. And so the Crown charged in courts-martial: "For mutinous conduct . . . in that coming to the knowledge of an intended mutiny in Her

17

Majesty's forces . . . did not give information thereof to his commanding officer" and "For conduct to the prejudice of good order and military discipline in having . . . joined a treasonable and seditious society, called the Fenian Brotherhood, having for its object the levying of war against the Queen and subverting of the government of the country."

But in all Ireland and elsewhere in the free world, these seven were hailed as patriots, guilty only of love of country and hatred of tyranny.

The sentence passed upon them by the Crown was death.

Death it would most certainly have been if fear had not struck Her Majesty's ministers. George William Frederick Charles, Duke of Cambridge, Commander-in-Chief of the Queen's Armies, had pleaded to his cousin, the Queen, that the death sentences be carried out with dispatch, to preserve British Army discipline. But Lord Derby and his cabinet, fearful not of their consciences but of what effect the executions might have on world trade if the harsh demands of His Grace were carried out, persuaded Her Majesty to commute the sentences of death to transport beyond the seas and a lifetime of hard labor. The Duke of Cambridge went into a pet that lasted for weeks.

The seven condemned men were Robert Cranston, Thomas Darragh, Michael Harrington, Thomas Hassett, Martin Hogan, James Wilson, and John Boyle O'Reilly. All were Irish, all were patriots, all were Fenians, sworn in secret bond to shed blood to set Ireland free.

What little luck of the Irish there was in Portland that early morning of October 15, 1867 clung tenaciously to two of these seven—sallow-faced Mike Harrington and grinning Tom Hassett. Their consecutive convict numbers had put them next each other in chain and dungeon, from Dublin's Royal Barracks to Mountjoy, to Pentonville, through the terribly solitary confinement of Millbank and now to Portland. The pair had been brought to Portland by steam train from Millbank twelve hours before.

With the suddenness of doom, guards shot back bolts, yanked iron doors open, strode into cells and kicked shivering occupants awake. Harrington was the first in his cell row to be routed from slumber. A warder's copper-toed boot brought him up from his planks snarling. He stumbled into the corridor, his fetters almost tumbling him. In a moment he was joined by Hassett, who had been just as harshly hauled from his cell.

As cell after cell was emptied, the normal bedlam in Portland Prison rose to pandemonium. Guards roared. Fists thudded against flesh. Prisoners howled.

Through the corridors trusties trundled barrows of food for the morning meal—a pint of cold oatmeal and potato gruel, a hunk of sour bread the size of a small boy's fist, a mug of watery cocoa.

Harrington and Hassett were wolfing down the mess as the pimply youth who had guard duty at their cell doors swaggered toward them.

"We've seen the last of the like of you," he said with a smirk.

"Could we depend on that, we'd be thankful and happy," Harrington jeered.

"Depend on it, you're for Australia today."

"Australia?" Hassett flicked an exploring cockroach from his sleeve. "How would a dolt like you know anything about such matters of state? Did Queen Victoria herself dispatch her own royal Knight of the Bottom to tell you to bid your guests in this hotel prepare for a healthful voyage to a foreign clime?"

"I don't understand you," the boy said, "but you're for the convict ship today, all right. She's the *Hougoumont* and she's waiting down harbor ready to take you."

Hassett rubbed the stubble on his brown head, where the hair had been torn out by the roots when he was pitch-capped—his head covered with melted pitch—by English warders in the Provost's Prison in Dublin's Royal Barracks. "Good enough," he said slowly. "Australia's just far enough away from this damned England to suit me."

"The lad is right," Harrington agreed. "They'd not boot us out of our cozy beds so early this morning just to see our faces by candlelight. What worries me is, will the rest of the boys be making this voyage with us?"

19

Hassett's face lit up. "On the train coming down yesterday I heard—mind you, it may not be true—that someone named O'Reilly had escaped from Dartmoor but had got himself caught again. That would be Boyle himself. The O'Reilly's not one to sit moping in an English jail. They don't make their prisons tough enough for him, nor for Jim Wilson neither. It sounds just like O'Reilly, getting out of that spot. Now maybe some more of us were at Dartmoor. There was a trainload coming here from the 'moor by train today, and . . ."

Shouts of "Chains! Chains!" cut him off. Into the musty corridors trusties began dragging lengths of new iron chains. Armorers and warders booted order into the chaos and began shackling the wrists and ankles of screaming women. In three chains, ten to each, they whimpered against the walls while 260 men—murderers, thieves, pimps, cheats, political prisoners—were manacled in similar fashion, all in order of registered numbers.

Harrington, No. 9757, and Hassett, No. 9758, were fastened one behind the other. An armorer knocked off their leg fetters.

In the wind-racked harbor, Her Majesty's Ship *Hougoumont*, Moulmein-built converted merchantman, strained to her two bow anchors as if anxious to get about the sordid business ahead. She carried the broad arrow of the convict ship whitely on the 153 feet of her black hull. Her teak decks glistened in a rain so heavy the marine at her gangway could scarcely make out the white yards of her royals. The rain tore in sheets along her deck and cascaded off her furled canvas. Under the cabin overhang, a young lieutenant tried to keep at least part of his uniform dry.

"Ahoy, the *Hougoumont*!"

A ship's longboat emerged from the gloom. The voice came louder: "Ahoy, the *Hougoumont*! Surgeon-General Brownlow requests permission to come aboard!"

The dripping lieutenant snapped to attention as the boat's crew made fast. A gray-haired man in the uniform of Her Majesty's Royal Navy picked his way up the slippery stairs, took the stiff salute of the lieutenant with a genial smile and said, "I'll see Captain Cousins at once."

His nostrils twitched as he entered the companionway. Despite the burning of sulfur candles and the sprinkling of lime, there clung to the *Hougoumont* the odor of the human cargo that had been all she had carried for the past two years. He held his breath momentarily, grimaced, breathed again. An earlier voyage in the *Hougoumont* had taught him his nose would grow accustomed to the smell—a smell that would be a stench in the tropics.

Captain Cousins rose from an armchair as the surgeon entered. The two officers shook hands as old friends. The surgeon looked appreciatively at the polished mahogany, the gleaming silver, the shining glassware and snow-white linen.

"Good morning, Captain," he said. "Though what's good about it is beyond my poor intellect to fathom. This rain chills the marrow. A fever-breeder if I ever saw one, my word as a physician on it." He looked around the cabin again. "It *is* pleasant here."

"A dirty morning, indeed," Captain Cousins agreed, "and the glass still falls. I hope we get all our cargo stowed before the wind swings foul." He turned to the sideboard and poured two brandies. "We embark three hundred-odd convicts, male and female, this voyage—feed them, sleep them, exercise them, teach them Royal Navy discipline and deliver them to Fremantle, West Australia. A straight ferrying task, sir! A ten-thousand-mile ferrying task."

Mr. Brownlow nodded slowly, savoring his brandy. "Captain, have you looked at the manifest for this 'cargo'!?"

"Can't say as I have, sir."

"Look closely, Captain. You'll find you have some special convicts aboard the *Hougoumont* this voyage."

"Convicts are all alike on my ship. You've sailed with me before. What have these scum specialized in? Murder? Rape? Arson?"

"Worse than that, Captain. Treason!"

Captain Cousins raised a bushy eyebrow. "Treason, Mr. Brown-low? That *is* special."

"Treason in Ireland to overthrow Her Majesty's government there and usurp it for wild revolutionaries!"

Captain Cousins fingered his glass thoughtfully. "Ah, the Irish military traitors. I heard about them and their 'Rising' when we docked. Well, they'll get nothing special here—unless they plot aboard my ship. I'll have them triced to the triangle so fast their heads will swim. And you, sir, can have the privilege of bringing them back to life after they're flogged—if you care to."

"But if they plot . . ."

"On my ship?" Captain Cousins looked at the surgeon incredulously, then laughed belly-hearty. "Come now, Mr. Brownlow, don't be fearsome. I promise you they'll all be meek as Irish lambs by the time we fetch Australia. I've a 'cat'—and a sovereign—that says I'm right."

He reached for the decanter. "A toast, sir! To Her Most Gracious Majesty, our sovereign Queen Victoria, long may she live, long may she rule and may God bless her . . . and may He damn to everlasting hell such as these who were traitors to her!"

In Portland Prison it was past six.

The chief warder's voice echoed through the corridors: "Convicts! Stand! Attention! Ready! March!"

The gates of the prison's main portal swung open. To the steady beat of drums and the rasping of iron against stone, the chains emerged. A soldier, bayonet fixed, headed every third chain.

In spite of the early hour, a silent crowd had gathered to get a last look at the wretches on their way to exile. In the drenched throng were some who had come hoping for a last glimpse of a loved one. A hoarse whisper, "Here they come," grew in volume.

The convicts trudged down the cobbled hill in a sort of shuffling dance. First in line were the females, next the twenty-six chains of men.

Every so often a shriek broke from someone in the crowd, followed by a rush to touch, to kiss, to speak. Then a shove from the butt of a musket, a heartless laugh and silent tears.

Harrington and Hassett were in the twentieth chain. As they emerged from the main gate, Harrington turned his head slightly back toward Hassett.

"Any of the rest in chain?"

"I've a plan, m'lad," Hassett whispered.

Before he could explain, a guard turned menacingly. Both prisoners watched his slow progress along the chains.

Then, startlingly clear over the shuffle of feet and the clanking of chains, Hassett's tenor voice rang out:

> "Out from many a mud-walled cabin
>   Eyes were watchin' through the night;
> Many a manly chest was throbbin'
>   For the blessed warnin' light.
> Murmurs passed along the valleys . . ."

"Who's that yowlin'?" The sentry raced back. "Shut up or I'll slit your throat with my bayonet!"

From far ahead, down the cobbled hill, came:

> "Like the banshee's lonely croon
>   And a thousand blades were flashin'
> At the Rising of the Moon."

"Darragh! By all that's holy, it's Tom Darragh! I'd know that voice anywhere," Harrington exulted.

Another voice caught up the song:

> "There beside the singin' river
>   That dark mass of men was seen . . .
> Far . . ."

Again the singer was cut off by the angry shout of a guard. But another voice picked up the song:

"Far above the shinin' weapons
    Hangs our own beloved Green.
Death to every foe and traitor
    Forward strike the marchin' tune . . ."

And a last triumphant voice shouted:

"And hurrah, me boys, for Freedom!
    'Tis the Rising of the Moon."

Then, loud and clear, "Erin go bragh!" broke from a chain waiting on the quay.

Tears ran down Harrington's face. "Cranston! Hogan! O'Reilly! And that last cheer—'twas Jim Wilson. All of us are here, Tom."

With the back of his hand the sentry fetched Harrington a clout over the face. "I said shut up, goddam you. Let out so much as a peep again, I'll stick you through."

Blood trickled from Harrington's nose down into his beard. He turned to Tom Hassett. "That's what I love about the English. They're so kind and gentle to poor captive people. . . . Well, a bit of blood was worth it. Now we know!"

At quayside, soldiers, warders and sailors shoved and cursed the convicts aboard a small paddle-wheel steamer that puffed her through the murk to the black-hulled convict ship. Tar-queued sailors made her fast, and chain after chain of convicts stumbled up the gangway stairs and stood dumbly on the deck, staring about them as their chains were knocked off.

Forward, running out to the foot of the bowsprit from within a few yards of the foremast, a V-shaped section of the main deck was roofed over, the wide end of the "V" latticed with inch-thick iron bars. This was the ship's punishment cell. Strapped to the foremast itself a black gaff stood out against the sky. In it two iron rings were set as wide apart as a man's arms could be stretched. In the deck below were two more iron rings, just as far apart and bolted down. This was the "triangle" for flogging. Above the triangle and tied about the foremast was a new hempen rope ending in a hangman's noose. Two of the main cargo hatches

were open. Over each was an iron cage with barred door. At
each cage stood two marines and a prison warder.

Harsh voices called out registered numbers. As each convict
answered, he joined a line that sank into the bowels of the ship.
Harrington and Hassett, among the last to descend, stood blink-
ing at the foot of the ladder. Out of the howling crowd a man
shoved forward. Reaching their side, he said, simply, "Tom! Mike!
Welcome aboard!"

Hassett cried out in joy. "Jim Wilson!" He threw his arms
around the man.

"Didn't you hear me on the hill? I shouted my guts out. Come
on, the rest of the boys are waiting."

He led them through a bulkhead door into a smaller compart-
ment of the forward hold, where they found Darragh, Cranston,
Hogan, and O'Reilly.

O'Reilly hugged the two newcomers. "God alone knows how
glad I am you're here and we're all together again."

On the deck anchor chains screeched through hawsepipes. Sails
sheeted home to crackle in the wind. A straining of rigging, a
creaking of timbers, and the *Hougoumont* stood for the narrow
opening in the mole, for the English Channel and the open sea.
A great hush fell on the prisoners in the crowded hold as the lift
of the seas took the ship. This was the beginning of the fateful
words the judges had spelled out—"transportation beyond the
seas."

Among the Fenians, "Red" Darragh was first to break the spell.
"Our past is past, that's sure. What's ahead can be no worse, now."

"There was a time I wasn't sure I had any future ahead at all,"
Wilson said grimly.

O'Reilly cleared his throat:

> "Take my heart's blessing over to dear Eire's strand
>   And the fair hills of Eire O.
> "To the remnant that love her—our forefather's land—
>   Fair hills of Eire O.
> "How sweet sing the birds, o'er mount there and vale,
>   Like soft sounding chords that lament for the Gael

25

And I o'er the surge, far, far away must wail
    The fair hills of Eire O."

Tears crept down Hogan's cheeks. He wiped them away as O'Reilly finished. "That was grand, Boyle, just grand."

"Some day I'm going to string words like pearls, just as that poet did. Some day I'll put words to paper and they'll sing a song. Maybe that will be my way to bring freedom to Ireland."

"It's a farewell to a rotten England I want to say," Cranston cut in, "farewell to an England I despise with all my heart and soul."

"Despise her we all do," Wilson said. "But right now we ought to get organized, plan what we're to do."

"Right, Jim," Hogan agreed. "Set up a captain——"

"Moved, seconded and carried. Jim Wilson is our captain," O'Reilly interrupted. The rest nodded.

Wilson stepped forward, pointed to each of the men in turn. "Once we're settled in quarters, Red, swipe some more blankets, and get some planks or boxes to sit on. . . . Boyle, you look to some extra tallow dips. . . . Mike, you're a baker, see what extra you can dig up better than the slop they'll hand us. Bob, you and Tom here, let's us try to grab us a corner we can call our own. Then we can take time out to do our bit of despising of 'dear old England.'"

2 . Go Accurst

Hell began aboard the *Hougoumont* at precisely half after eight o'clock the morning she sailed. At that hour she moved her stubby bow out from Portland Harbor into the teeth of as savage a Channel storm as Captain Cousins had ever experienced in his forty-odd years at sea.

The wind and rain worsened as the last of the ship's human cargo was bullied down the hatches. By the time the *Hougoumont* had lurched into the Channel and wore ship for her southwesterly course to clear the Channel Islands and the Scillys, a tremendous tidal rip and mountainous seas tore at her hull. Within a half hour all hatches were battened down against the white water that sheeted the length of her reeling deck. Seamen raced aloft to take in sail, but despite the officers' cries for speed, the foreroyal split with a resounding crack before the men could hand it. Under fore, main and mizzen courses, topsails and jib the ship shuddered along.

Few of the prisoners had ever before been to sea. Wails of terror at the unknown were compounded with sobs of despair. Slop buckets overflowed, then spewed their contents over the planks. Each pitch and each roll hurled dozens sprawling across the splintery decking. Blood flowed from countless cuts. Shins, elbows, skulls cracked against timbers.

In this devil's din, the seven Fenians clung to the corner they had picked out to defend as their castle. Warders had thrust them into the forward hold with the hardened criminals—murderers, thieves, arsonists. There Wilson, with his quick eye to vantage points, had chosen a spot where one of the few whale-oil lamps

guttered and where hammocks could be disposed. None was sea-
sick; long experience on army transports had accustomed them.

News of the conditions below took long hours to penetrate the
rarer atmosphere of officers' country. It was late on the second
nightmarish day that Surgeon Brownlow, with a medical aide,
made his way down the forecastle ladder into the male prisoners'
quarters.

He was momentarily appalled at the need for medical care. A
barked order sent his aide scurrying topside. He was back in a
few minutes with a whispered message.

The doctor frowned. "Broken arm? Too bad. He would have
been most helpful. We'll have to 'press some of these more rugged-
looking men here." He eyed the few still on their feet. "You . . .
you . . . you . . ." His finger pointed out Darragh, Hogan and
Cranston. "You look well enough. Step forward, you three."

The three hesitated, then at a nod from Wilson, stepped out
a pace.

"Names?"

"Thomas Darragh."

"Michael Hogan."

"Robert Cranston."

"Say 'sir' when you speak to your betters."

Silence greeted his order. The surgeon did not stress the point.

"So you're the Irish traitors, eh?"

None replied.

"I never thought I'd deal with traitors." Brownlow shrugged
his shoulders. "You men should know something about binding
up wounds. You were all soldiers, weren't you?"

More silence.

Brownlow pointed to Hogan. "Speak up, man."

"Yes," Hogan muttered.

Brownlow turned to his aide. "Take these men topside and load
them with splints and bandages."

By lamplight the surgeon and his new aides dressed the wounds
and splinted the limbs of more than two score prisoners. As they

finished, Brownlow said: "Shouldn't say thanks to traitors, I suppose. But . . . good job, lads!"

In spite of the storm, rigid Royal Navy discipline ruled the *Hougoumont*. A midshipman, imprisoned in the main deck punishment cell the first day out for refusing to climb aloft on the swaying mainmast, was taken out the third day quite dead, of "exposure and ingestion of a quantity of sea water," the surgeon determined. His body was hurried overside with the shortest of committal services.

It was three days before the *Hougoumont* had battered her way through the Channel storm and, all canvas set again—topsails, topgallants, royals, skysails, jib and staysails—was on course south. Morning of the fourth day saw the midships hatch cover raised and windsails set to force a little fresh air into the stifling depths of the ship. Able-bodied prisoners were set at scrubbing. Lime was sprinkled about. Sulfur candles were ignited.

The morning of the fourth day, too, Captain Cousins decided it was time to stop coddling the convicts. From then on, for the duration of the voyage, at ten each morning, all miscreants caught violating ship's rules were brought before the mast, their crimes listed by a boatswain's mate and sentences pronounced by the captain himself. By noon sentences had been carried out. The bloodied "cat" was back in its place beside the foremast gaff. Convicts holystoned the red-stained deck under the "triangle." Those sentenced to the main deck punishment cell were set to picking oakum behind its inch-thick bars, their fare bread and water.

As the seas moderated, the prisoners, under heavy armed guard, were brought on deck in groups of fifty and marched briskly about the fore and main hatches for a half hour.

The *Hougoumont* put in at Funchal for fresh water, potatoes, vegetables, good bottled Madeira wine for the officers and the passengers, and casks of cheap red wine and lemons to ward off scurvy from crew and convicts. Southward then, with good winds and balmy weather toward Ascension Island, St. Helena and Capetown.

Day followed interminable day. On one of them Mike Harrington dumped his pannikin of food in disgust. "It's worse than the rotten slop they fed us at Dartmoor. With one hand tied behind my back and with my eyes blinded, I'll cook better than the sea-swab that hashed up this mess." Which outburst got him fifty lashes, a bloody back—and a job as helper in the ship's galley where the storm had taken its toll of broken limbs too. Plenty of scraps of good food went under his shirt and found their way into the common store in the Fenian stronghold in the forehold.

Red Darragh, lone Protestant among the seven, became assistant to the Church of England chaplain and led the prayer the prisoners had to offer each evening: "O God, who art the arbiter of the destiny of nations and who rulest the world in Thy great wisdom, look down, we beseech Thee, from Thy holy place on the sufferings of our poor country. Scatter her enemies, O Lord, and confound their evil prophets. Hear us, O God, hear the earnest cry of our people, and give them strength and fortitude to dare and suffer in their holy cause. Send her help, O Lord, from the holy place. And from Zion protect her. Amen."

Surgeon Brownlow, in his inspection visits to the prison quarters, discovered that of the convicts few but the Fenians had outstanding intellect. He was interested in O'Reilly in particular, whom he found well educated and, through his apprenticeship on the Drogheda *Argus,* with a distinct journalistic bent. At O'Reilly's request, the surgeon provided him with pen, ink and paper. O'Reilly began editing the first of what was to be seven issues of *The Wild Goose,* named for those Irish soldiers of fortune who in foreign climes had fought with the enemies of England.

One night while the *Hougoumont* was plodding between Ascension and St. Helena, O'Reilly called his friends together into the circle of light the lamp gave the corner where they had slung their hammocks. After reading the "news" in the single-sheet copy of *The Wild Goose,* he began diffidently: "I have strung a few words together into a sort of poem for this issue. It is a poor thing and only half done, but I shall try to finish it for our next issue. Do you care to hear the first part of it now?"

"Read it, Boyle, read it. It can be no worse than the news, which were somewhat less than that," Darragh quipped.

O'Reilly cleared his throat. "'The Flying Dutchman,'" he announced, "by John Boyle O'Reilly.

"Long time ago, from Amsterdam, a vessel sailed away,
    As fair a ship as ever flung aside the laughing spray.
Upon the shore were tearful eyes and scarfs were in the air,
    As to her o'er the Zuyder Zee went fond adieu and prayer.
And brave hearts yearning shoreward from the outward going
    ship,
    Felt lingering kisses clinging to tear-wet cheek and lip.
She sailed for some far eastern clime and as she skimmed the seas,
    Each tapered mast was bending like a rod before the
      breeze . . ."

As he continued his tale of Captain Vanderdecken and his bout with a terrific storm, O'Reilly's voice took fire. He fairly shouted the Dutch skipper's challenge to God:

"Howl on, ye winds! Ye tempests, howl! Your rage is spent in vain!
    Despite your strength, your frowns, your hate, I'll ride upon
      the main!
Defiance to your idle shrieks, I'll sail upon my path,
    I cringe not for thy Maker's smile, I care not for His wrath . . ."

Then, fearfully, O'Reilly recited the words from the Almighty:

"The judgment words swept o'er the sea, 'Go wretch, accurst,
    condemned,
    Go sail forever on the deep by shrieking tempests hemmed.
No home, no port, no calm, no rest, no gentle fav'ring breeze,
    Shall ever greet thee! Go accurst, and battle with the seas!'"

The next issue of the *Goose* carried the completion of the poem with its final stanza:

"The doom of those is sealed to whom the Phantom ship appears,

31

They'll never reach their destined port, they'll see their home
no more,
They who see the Flying Dutchman—never, never reach the
shore!"

The *Hougoumont* seemed more and more the phantom ship as
she coursed along, a grim ship on a grim errand.

She sighted other ships on the ocean highways—and they
sighted her. But the menacing broad arrow on her hull made her
accurst on the sea. There were no friendly trumpet hails, no
leisurely gams—those friendly visits between officers and men of
ships that crossed paths on the deep. Other skippers wanted no
contact with a convict ship's stinking cargo. And Captain Cousins had neither the time nor the inclination to dally as he drove
his ship toward her goal.

In the six thousand miles from the Channel to the Cape of Good
Hope, the *Hougoumont* passed many other vessels, even if they
did not hail; but in the four thousand-odd miles of her easterly
course to fetch the coast of West Australia, she might indeed have
been a spectral ship on a ghostly sea. The illusion held even to
the moment she bore silently into a mist-shrouded Fremantle
harbor at three in the morning of Friday, January 10, 1868, and
lay to for the break of day.

Cranston, a light sleeper always, woke to the strange feeling
of cessation of motion, and the muffled creak of yards being braced
about. With his foot he touched the bare bottom of Wilson, who
was snoring in the hammock next to his. Wilson spun over in his
canvas sack and growled: "Why the hell are you waking me?"

"We've come to Australia, that's why!"

"Do you think I give a tinker's damn for the whole of the goddam country, let alone one part of it?"

"Don't you want to see it?"

"There's gold in Australia," young Cranston ventured softly.

"Gold! You got as much chance getting your hands on gold as
I got making my fortune raising pigs in Kildare. Stop thinking
of this fine Australia and get to thinking of how we're getting out
of it. That's what I'm thinking all the time."

"Right, Jim," O'Reilly said. "I'm getting away. The English don't make a prison that can hold me. I got away at Dartmoor and I'd be back in Ireland if it hadn't been for an informer. I'll get away from Fremantle."

The *Hougoumont* lay to offshore until the sun rose above the peaks of the Darling Mountains, far inland. Then, in contrast to her stormy departure from England, she glided toward Victoria Quay on a breeze so light it scarcely riffled the clear harbor water.

Captain Cousins eased his ship's hull alongside the new government quay. The heavy-leaded monkey fists of the heaving lines thudded against the planks of the dock, where waiting hands grabbed them and hauled hawsers ashore to make them fast to the bollards. Amidships a gangplank was shoved shoreward. The iron gates at the hatches were unlocked and opened. Armed marines lined the deck from hatches to gangway.

After about a half hour a cloud of white dust arose a distance ashore. Down the street leading to the wharf a platoon of the Enlisted Pensioners' Reserve swung smartly to the quay and took up positions from the end of the *Hougoumont's* gangplank to the end of the dock.

Two by two, the convicts were prodded up the iron ladders to blink in the sunlight. Shoved across the deck, they stumbled down the gangplank and onto the quay. There they were lined up, again two by two, to await the Reserve Captain's orders.

There were no chains. No attempt was made to form the convict line in order of registered numbers. It was no trouble for the Fenians to keep together. They stood well at the head of the waiting line and so had a good chance to look at the town of Fremantle.

The town was a collection of one- and two-story houses and business places, built mostly of wood and wood-shingled, with here and there a few constructed of limestone and sandstone. Surmounting a slight elevation a few blocks back from the busy waterfront shops were some imposing buildings, evidently residences for officials or for well-to-do businessmen and tradesmen. Above, and dwarfing the rest of the town's buildings, was a huge, star-shaped, walled, limestone structure that needed no sign to proclaim it Her Majesty's Penal Colony—"The Establishment," as the Fenians soon found out it was called.

Hassett cast a critical eye on it. "Well," he said judiciously, "'tis no Dublin and that's a fact."

The last of the convicts were delivered to the dock by the *Hougoumont's* marine guards. The Reserve Captain cast a military eye along the double line and over his men.

"Ready! March!"

The long double line shuffled shoreward. Over the rail of the *Hougoumont* Captain Cousins, Surgeon-General Brownlow and the rest of the ship's officers on duty watched. The surgeon gave a halfhearted wave of his hand. Only O'Reilly, far ahead at the shore end of the quay, caught the salute and answered it.

The *Hougoumont's* "ten-thousand-mile ferrying job" was ended.

Through dust like a bitter cloud the line snaked its way from shore uphill toward the prison.

"So the English call this thing a prison," Wilson scoffed as he eyed the buildings ahead. "I could step over such walls. The dungeon's got to be mighty deep and strong to pen me in that place!"

Hearing him, one of the reserves said grimly: "Ah, you can get out all right, lad. That's the easy part. But you can't stay out and that's God's truth."

"A pound on that!" Wilson snapped.

The guard shook his head. "Keep your shillings—if you have any. You can't win that bet."

The walls were indeed not much higher than would have shut in the garden of an English estate. Outside, and to the left of a heavy, iron-studded wooden gate, an ancient fieldpiece pointed drunkenly into the sky. As the head of the convict line reached the wall, the gate swung open.

Inside was a motley collection of buildings that included a three-story structure surmounted by a carved stone cylinder for ornament, smaller barracks, storehouses, a Church of England chapel, several two-story residences and some guardhouses. All were clustered about a large parade ground. From a staff a British flag drifted lazily in the light morning air. A few trees cast sparse, speckled shadows on the glittering white of the crushed limestone walks and the parade.

The reserves herded the prisoners onto the parade ground and formed them into a rough, double line, all facing a rostrum-like stone block. A stocky, gray-haired, red-faced man in a suit of whites, with a tropical helmet shading his watery blue eyes, strode army-style from one of the buildings and mounted the rostrum. Glancing along the line of prisoners, he cleared his throat mightily and said:

"I want your undivided attention. That is my first order.

"My name is Donan. I am superintendent of this Establishment. I am the representative of Her Majesty Queen Victoria's government in this penal colony. As her royal representative, my word is law.

"I am a fair man. If you behave, you will receive fair treatment. If you do not obey orders, you will discover that we have in this prison colony a code which provides the most severe penalties. You will learn that I do not hesitate to carry out these penalties to the utmost.

"Mark well my words!

"For refusal to obey any order of a prison official, the punishment is flogging, extension of sentence and solitary confinement.

"For refusal to perform any task while on work detail, the punishment is flogging, extension of sentence and solitary confinement.

"For attempt to escape from any work party engaged in lawful prison activities outside the walls of the prison, the punishment may be death or extension of sentence, flogging and solitary confinement.

"For attempt to escape from the confines of the prison, the punishment is death.

"For theft of any article whatsoever in Her Majesty's storehouses, buildings, camps, the punishment is death.

35

"For any attempt, whether successful or not, to destroy by fire the property of Her Majesty, the punishment is death.

"For the accidental killing of a prison official, the punishment is death.

"For the willful murder of a prison officer, the punishment is death."

Donan paused. He glared at the prisoners, then resumed:

"If you are accused of any infraction of the rules or of discipline in this prison, I am the judge and I am the jury. I will hear the charges brought against you and I will render the verdict. There is no appeal from my judgment."

Again he paused. Again his eyes looked over the prisoners. The convicts shuffled a bit, then stiffened as the superintendent held up his hand for silence.

"Many of you say to yourselves: 'Those penalties will never apply to me. I will escape.'

"There is no doubt you will have plenty of opportunities to escape. If you are not being punished—and we have dungeons in which to pen you up when you are being punished—you will often be assigned to work parties outside the walls. You may work on the jetties, or you may be assigned to a road gang or a timber gang. You will think it easy to get away.

"But, if you do run away, you will be caught or you will perish."

Wilson turned a dark scowling face toward Hogan, standing next to him. "He's bluffing. I got it planned right now. If I can't break clean out of his little pipsqueak prison . . ."

The heavy right hand of a warder clamped down hard on his shoulder. Wilson winced. The warder shot his left hand aloft in signal. With scarcely a break in his harangue, the superintendent said loudly: "Fifty lashes! Talking in ranks!"

A second guard ran up to the first. Between them they dragged Wilson away. It happened so fast Hogan could only gulp.

Donan went on smoothly:

"I repeat, you will be caught or you will perish.

"There are two ways to escape from this prison. To save you the trouble of thinking this out for yourselves, you can get away by the sea or by the land.

"So you will say, perhaps, 'I will escape by land.'

"There are mountains in back of you. Just beyond them is the most cruel country God ever turned over to the Devil. It is a country of deserts, salt lakes, bitter springs, sun-parched plains, red-hot rocks. It is a country in which nothing lives—in which you cannot live.

"Even to reach this hellish country you will first have to penetrate dense forests, where poisonous insects and death-dealing snakes lurk. You can go mad from the stings of those insects. You can die from the fangs of those venomous snakes.

"Perhaps you will manage, somehow, to survive these horrors. You will reach the desert on the other side of the mountains. There you will most certainly die of terrible thirst and slow starvation—unless I find you.

"And I will start searching for you the moment you are posted as missing. While you are wandering, confused, thirsting, starving, dying, I will have trackers on your trail. These trackers are aborigines. They are natives of the bush country. They can trace the spoor of a man through forests, over barren ground, over sun-baked rocks. They will find you. If you are still alive, they will drag you back. If you are dead, you will not be worth dragging back, and they will call to the carrion birds to feast on your carcass.

"Suppose you try to escape by sea. It looks easy. There are ships at the quay. There are ships standing offshore. There are passing ships not too far at sea. But you will find that no English shipmaster will conceal you aboard his ship. For one thing, there is a price on your head that will be well worth his while to gain. That and his duty to his Queen will be sufficient to impel him to give you up.

"Perhaps you think you can swim to some passing ship of foreign registry. I tell you now that the waters here abound in sharks the size of which would stagger your most vivid imagination. Those sharks wait to rip you to shreds.

"Escape from this prison is impossible.

"You have been warned. Do not be foolhardy enough to try to get away.

"Warders, form work parties. Feed prisoners. Assign quarters. Work begins immediately."

Superintendent Donan stepped smartly from the stone rostrum and strode into the prison offices.

The Reservists marched out of the yard. The big gate swung shut. The warders began to split the prisoners into gangs.

O'Reilly whispered to Darragh: "There'll be a way. There has to be a path to liberty. I swear it, Red, I swear I'll find that path."

3 . A Captain's Word

For the forlorn prisoners in Her Gracious Majesty Queen Victoria's Penal Colony in Fremantle, West Australia, days were weeks and weeks were months and then were years.

In Ireland the star of Charles Stewart Parnell rose on Freedom's horizon. England's Prime Minister William Ewart Gladstone, confessing the fear instilled in him by the Fenians, allowed the Land Act to become law.

General U. S. Grant, who had led the victory of freedom over slavery, became the eighteenth President of the United States. A golden railroad spike driven at Promontory, Utah, joined the Atlantic and the Pacific Oceans with an iron band, and women gained freedom to vote in Wyoming. Napoleon III surrendered at Sedan, and Léon Gambetta escaped from Paris by balloon. The Doctrine of Papal Infallibility was proclaimed, and in Ireland the Established (English) Church was disestablished.

Victor Emmanuel II seized Rome, and the Pope became the "prisoner of the Vatican." Wilhelm I of Hohenzollern became Kaiser of Germany and France lost Alsace by the Treaty of Frankfurt that ended the Franco-Prussian War.

Henry Stanley found Dr. Livingstone in the wilds of Darkest Africa, and Mrs. O'Leary's cow kicked over a lantern and set Chicago afire. The Panic of 1873 tore the heart out of New York's financial world. Edward Stokes shot Jim Fiske to death, and Boss Tweed came to the end of his racketeering days.

In the Establishment—John Boyle O'Reilly found "the path."

In New Bedford, Massachusetts, a burly young man in a seaman's peajacket slipped on icy granite paving and almost fell.

39

Regaining his footing, he strode on, shaking his head. Never would he get used to these confounded sidewalks. Give him the honest deck of a whaler, blubber-slippery though it might be.

George Smith Anthony was confused and out of sorts that chilly February night in 1875. Some fool's errand he was on, surely—a fitting end to a tormenting day that had started out prosaically enough with a good-by kiss from his young wife as he started to work, and finally had brought him into such a mental snarl that he scarcely knew what course he was sailing.

"Evening, Cap'n Anthony," a passer-by said, genially yet respectfully, touching a finger to his cap.

Anthony responded with but a half glance at the well-wisher.

"Cap'n Anthony" indeed! Any tomfool who could row a skiff from New Bedford across the Acushnet River to Fairhaven was "captain." It was "Cap'n This" and "Cap'n That" from morning till night, enough to turn a man's stomach.

As far as George Anthony himself was concerned, he figured he hadn't a right to such a title, not now, with his feet anchored to the ground like any landlubber.

A great deal had happened since that day three years ago when he had seen the lines made fast to the dock and had stepped ashore from the deck of the whaling ship *Hope On* into the arms of his bride-to-be with the promise that he'd never go to sea again. A good marriage it was indeed for him, for his Emmie was the daughter of John S. Richardson, well-to-do ship outfitter and agent. With the lay from the sale of whale oil and spermaceti from the *Hope On's* highly successful two-year cruise, Anthony had bought a house on Second Street, with a fan-lighted doorway and a view of bustling New Bedford Harbor. He'd got a shore-side job with the Morse Twist Drill Company, makers of tools and dies—a good job. Now, there was baby Sophie, named for her maternal grandmother. Innocent little Sophie was one of the reasons he was out of sorts that frosty night.

That noon he had unexpectedly met up with Jonathan Bourne, the owner of the *Hope On*, who looked on George Anthony almost as a son, for he himself had picked George to be master of the whaler. It had been a good choice for all concerned. Mr. Bourne had mildly but earnestly scolded George for quitting the sea at the age of twenty-eight, and never lost an opportunity to rub it in. Wednesday, the twenty-fourth day of February, 1875, George Anthony was thirty-one years old.

For three years his pledge to quit the sea had loomed larger and larger as day followed day—humdrum, as much alike as mackerel in a school. Not too long ago, he had actually ventured to his father-in-law that he wouldn't mind considering a command—oh, not now, but later on—when Sophie was older—that is, if a good command came along. John Richardson had looked at him a little queerly, he thought, but had said nothing.

The yellow glow of whale-oil lamps beckoned from his windows as he strode up the brick walk that was slippery with new-formed frost, and stepped into the snug kitchen.

He kissed Emmie, hung his cap and peajacket on a peg by the door. Month-old Sophie cooed in her basket near the kitchen table. Emmie and George leaned over her. George's arm stole around his wife's slim waist. He kissed a warm curl of the almost black hair at the nape of her neck.

Emmie started up suddenly. "The chowder!" she cried, and fled to the stove where a big iron pot simmered.

As they finished their supper with Indian pudding, Emmie said: "I almost forgot. Father sent word today that he wanted you to come down to the store this evening. He didn't say why, just that it was mighty important. At exactly eight o'clock!"

A new wave of discontent engulfed George Anthony. Here a man was ready and pining for a quiet evening at home with a loving wife at his side, a baby asleep in her crib, a log on the fire—the kind of evening a sea captain dreams about when he is ten thousand miles from home. He sighed.

Emmie sympathized. "I'm sorry, dear, but Father doesn't often ask favors. You'll go, won't you?"

George got back into his peajacket, pulled a blue knit watch-cap down over his chestnut hair, and set out for his father-in-law's store.

41

From Second Street he turned on Union. Ahead of him, all black and silver under a waxing moon, lay the harbor of the whaling capital of America. The riding lights of a hundred whalers, merchantmen, coastal schooners and fishing craft rocked on the tide.

It had grown colder. Anthony pulled his watch-cap down over his ears and snugged the peajacket tighter around his broad shoulders as he elbowed his way through the tide of boisterous seamen and blowzy women that surged at the doors of the saloons and bawdy houses. A drunken seaman lurched and almost knocked him down. He shoved the befuddled lad away and hurried on past Johnny Cake Hill. Around the corner, on Water Street, the windows of John Richardson's store shone ahead of him.

There was only one customer in the store. He was picking over a pile of heavy knit sweaters under the eye of Richardson. John nodded to George, almost mysteriously. The seaman made his choice, paid for it, finally touched his forehead in salute and was gone.

"Evenin', George!" Richardson said, but gave George no time to reply. Quickly he stepped outside. The heavy iron shutters banged. He came in, closed the stout wooden door, shot the bolt home, then bolted the shutters. After extinguishing all but one of the big whale-oil lamps, he turned the wick in that one down to a faint yellow glow.

"There's someone in my office wants to talk to you, George."

Behind the main storeroom, John Richardson had his ship's agent office, as familiar to George Anthony as his own parlor: a walnut desk with heavy, round-turned legs, four big drawers and two top cupboards; three sturdy chairs of pine, worn polished with age; shelves that held boxes of ship's papers, each lettered boldly and blackly with the name of a vessel—*Ocean Wave, Arethusa, Hope On, Mary Ann, Peru, Sarah B. Hale*; a small cast-iron safe with a huge brass padlock. On the wall was a tall barometer in a wooden case and beside it, dangling from an iron hook, a long iron tryrod with a small glass vial at the end for tasting whale oil. A whale-oil lamp swung from the ceiling, its twin wicks burning brightly. A potbelly stove glowed with greasy wood from a returned whaler's galley.

Henry C. Hathaway was perched on the edge of the desk. George had known him from childhood. Hathaway was chief of night police in New Bedford. He was about George Anthony's age, a big man with huge shoulders, a bull voice, piercing eyes set in a face deep bronzed from years at sea. Like most New Bedford boys, Henry Hathaway had shipped before the mast when he was barely fourteen years old. He had won his mate's papers, but then had quit the sea for the police job.

A stranger was seated in one of the chairs, his back partly to the lamp so that most of his heavily black-bearded face was in shadow. When George entered, the stranger rose and stood waiting.

"Captain Anthony," Hathaway said, "I want to make you acquainted with Mr. John Devoy of New York City and of the New York *Herald*. Mr. Devoy, sir, this is Captain George Anthony of whom I have spoken."

"My pleasure, Captain Anthony." Devoy's voice was deep-toned and cultivated. He clasped Anthony's proffered hand. For a long moment two men stood appraising each other.

Anthony saw a bearded man in his early thirties, slim and erect, a little taller than Anthony himself. His deep-set dark eyes gave him the look of a scholar. His bearing was that of a man who thought much, but could instantly translate his thoughts into action.

Devoy spoke first. "I am an Irishman, Captain Anthony. Many times my countrymen are accused of dramatizing insignificant circumstances. But I hope you will not think me dramatic when I say I think what we have to say to each other tonight is better said with the lights out!"

He turned and extinguished the whale-oil lamp. The office was plunged into momentary darkness. Then the glow from the stove took over.

"Won't you gentlemen please be seated?" Devoy said, remaining on his feet. "Captain Anthony," he continued, "before I go any further, I wish your solemn word that no matter what you hear tonight, no matter what comes of this meeting, you will keep it a secret until I myself release you from your pledge. The lives of many men depend on absolute secrecy. Mr. Hathaway and your father-in-law have given me their word. Do I have yours also?"

"Of course, sir."

"Thank you, Captain. I think you will understand later why I asked that pledge. I know you must be curious as to why I am here and why you are here. I want Mr. Hathaway to tell you."

Henry Hathaway leaned his big frame forward, clasped and unclasped his hamlike hands, then ran one hand through his shock of unruly hair.

"George," he began at last, "you are here because Mr. Devoy wanted to meet the best and most trustworthy whaling captain in New England. Don't deny it. When Mr. Devoy said he wanted a captain who could keep his mouth shut and who was brave and intelligent too, I knew you were the man."

George shook his head deprecatingly.

"Now I know you're wondering," Hathaway went on, "how Mr. Devoy ever heard about Henry Hathaway that he should be asking him to find such a man. It started when I was third officer of the *Gazelle*, Captain Gifford, whaling, out of New Bedford a half dozen years ago. Remember?"

"Of course. The voyage when you picked up that escaped convict."

Hathaway tried to keep his bull voice down. "Right! That man turned out to be John Boyle O'Reilly, now a great Boston editor and poet."

George nodded.

"I am proud that Mr. O'Reilly and I have been fast friends ever since that rescue and the voyage back home. I had a letter from Mr. O'Reilly a few days ago. He said a friend of his, a Mr. John Devoy, was going to come up from New York to New Bedford to see me, and asked me to do whatever I could for him. Mr. Devoy and I had a long talk. He asked me to recommend a whaling captain he could trust, who could keep his mouth shut, maybe even under torture. You are the man I recommended."

Hathaway sank breathlessly back in his chair, pulled a huge kerchief from his pocket and mopped his forehead.

Devoy nodded. "Thank you, Mr. Hathaway." He fixed his eyes on Anthony. "Now, Captain Anthony, you know why you are here this night. But you are still asking yourself 'what for,' are you not?"

"You have me puzzled."

"Captain, I ask a favor of you. From what I have learned from your father-in-law it is a great favor indeed. He has told me about the promise you made never to go to sea again—but I want you to command a whaling ship for me."

Anthony spoke quickly. "That is a simple request, sir. I see no reason for all this secrecy, nor any secrecy about my answer. It is 'no.' Thank you, sir, for all the compliments you have paid me—but no!" His hands spread in a gesture of finality.

"That really doesn't surprise me, Captain. Mr. Richardson told me what your immediate response would be."

"Mr. Richardson knows my answer will be the same no matter how many times you ask me," Anthony said. "I intend to keep my pledge to my wife. I will never go to sea again."

"I respect your pledge, Captain, and your good intentions. But Mr. Richardson seems to think that when you learn about this voyage you may wish to change your mind."

"With all due respect to my father-in-law, sir, I don't think he knows what he is talking about. You are wasting your time, Mr. Devoy." Captain Anthony started to rise.

"Wait, George!" Richardson's voice was urgent. "The least you can do is hear Mr. Devoy out. If I hadn't thought he had something worth while to say, I wouldn't have brought you down here tonight."

Anthony turned on him. "It seems to me, sir, that before Emmie and I were married you heartily approved of that promise of mine."

"Now, George, don't get angry," Richardson said. "I know all you say is true. But let's take this calm-like. Times—and men's minds—have been known to change before this. I seem to remember that only a few weeks ago you yourself talked to me about a command, didn't you?"

"I was thinking about years ahead, when Sophie's grown up." Anthony sank back in his chair, shaking his head stubbornly.

Devoy broke the tense silence. "Captain Anthony," he asked quietly, "have you any Irish blood in your veins?"

"No, sir. To the best of my knowledge I have not."

"So much the better. Now, let me see if I can give you an argument that will convince you that you should command our ship."

"You can argue me a hundred arguments, Mr. Devoy, but for every one I'll have the same answer."

Devoy nodded. "Captain, the more you talk against me, the more I realize you are the man for us. Your persistence strikes me as a most admirable quality indeed."

Anthony shrugged. "That's as may be, sir. Now, go on, if you have idle time, and argue." He settled back in his chair, watching the glow of the potbelly, puzzled at this futile word-play.

"My argument will be simple. It is based on a plain statement of facts. And the facts are freedom and hatred of tyranny. I think we can agree that they are most admirable facts."

"Yes, to that I would agree."

"Of course you favor freedom?"

"Certainly."

"And you hate tyranny?"

"What American would not?"

"You see, Captain, we agree again. We cannot argue."

"I'm not agreeing on anything. What can this talk of freedom and tyranny have to do with commanding a whaler?"

"I'll come around to that directly, Captain. But first, did you ever stop to realize what it means to be a free man in a free country? A hundred years ago Americans rose up against tyranny and won independence from the English. Then in 1812 you fought again and won the freedom of the seas for your vessels. By those two wars you gained liberty and you gained the right to form your own government. Some other countries have not been so lucky. Now, Captain, would you like to have your own chance to strike a blow in the cause of freedom?"

"What American would not?"

"Good! Captain, I have told you I am an Irishman. I am an Irish patriot. There is a price on my head. I was a rebel in the last Rising—which was not successful. Now, Captain, have you ever heard of the Fenians?"

"Vaguely. Some sort of Irish organization?" Anthony stirred impatiently in his chair. "Mr. Devoy, what on earth has all this got to do with me commanding a whaler for you?"

"Let me come to that in my own way, Captain. When an Irishman gets all wound up in his tale, you just have to let him unwind himself the best he can."

Anthony shrugged again.

"In 1865 the Fenians planned a revolution—we call them 'Risings.' It was the best organized Rising Ireland ever had. Our leader was James Stephens. His idea was to recruit not only civilians but all the Irish sympathizers in the Queen's regiments stationed in Ireland. Thus, when he passed the word to revolt, the regiments would rally to the cause, overthrow English rule and regain our country.

"I was one of those Stephens chose to organize the regimental recruiting. I had seven lieutenants, all of them soldiers in one or another of the regiments stationed in or around Dublin. Within a few months we had more than three quarters of the soldiery sworn in as members of the order, ready to rise at the word. All of them had taken the same oath." Devoy's voice took on a hushed tone. "Would you like to hear that oath, Captain?" Without waiting for reply he said, solemnly: "I, John Devoy, do solemnly swear allegiance to the Irish republic now virtually established; that I will take up arms at a moment's notice to defend its integrity and independence; that I will yield implicit obedience to the commands of my superior officers; and finally I take this oath in the spirit of a true soldier of Liberty. So help me God."

Devoy went on, "For command, Captain, we had more than

two hundred American Union officers in Dublin waiting to take charge. We had your President Johnson's assurance of full recognition of the Irish Republic and we had the promise of your General Philip Sheridan to be our field marshal.

"But everything went askew. The English got wind of the Rising. Thousands of Irishmen were arrested. The Americans fled. Thousands of prison terms were meted out. Thousands were deported. Thousands more fled to Canada and America. I was one of those who managed to escape."

Devoy was pacing the office. The little room had become insufferably hot. Richardson opened the firedoor to cool off the potbelly. The flames danced on the walls and glinted on the perspiring brow of the speaker. He mopped the beads from his forehead with an already limp kerchief. Captain Anthony leaned forward in his chair, now paying closest attention.

"In 1871," Devoy went on, "most Irish political prisoners were released and exiled. I see some of them every day of my life—proud men all, for they risked lives and fortunes for the cause of liberty. But the English are still bitter. Six men still must rot out their lives in a penal colony because they dared fight for freedom, just as you Americans did.

"I know these six men, Captain Anthony. They are my friends and my blood brothers. They were tried for their lives on the testimony of informers and spies. They were sentenced to hang, but the English, afraid of world opinion, gave them commutation of sentence to hard labor overseas. They suffered in the most vile prisons. They were jammed aboard a stinking convict ship with the dregs of the English criminal world. They were transported to an Australian penal colony, and there they waste their God-given lives this very day."

Devoy's voice rose vibrantly. "Captain Anthony, as I stand before you and before my God at this moment, I swear that these six men committed no crime save love of country, desire for freedom and hatred of tyranny."

Devoy sopped his brow again with the wet kerchief. His fingers trembled as he stuffed it back into his waistcoat pocket.

"Captain Anthony, we are ready with more than thirty thousand dollars in American gold to send an American whaleship, under your command, to Fremantle, Australia, and rescue these men!"

After a moment of bewilderment Anthony's words came tumbling out: "Surely you are joking, Mr. Devoy! The idea is—unfeasible."

"George, don't be so hasty!" Richardson broke in.

But Anthony leaped up. "If I understand you correctly, sir, you want me practically to invade an English colony. To do that you would need ships of the line—cannon—an army. I am a simple seaman, no admiral. Your plan is impossible, sir, utterly impossible!"

Devoy faced him with a half smile. "Bravo, Captain! Once more, you show an admirable quality that makes me realize you are our man. You can estimate dangers and face up to them."

"I'm not facing up to any dangers. I'm just pointing out that your plan won't work. Why, you could start a war!"

Hathaway laid a hand on his friend's arm. "It isn't as impossible as you think, George. Sit down and listen some more!"

Anthony resignedly sank back in his chair.

Devoy took over again. "I don't ask you to create an international incident. All we do ask is that you dare such units of the English Navy as may be in those waters when you arrive. We don't ask that you lead a landing party. We guarantee to deliver our men to you on a beach of your own choosing. Only then will it be up to you and your crew to take our men off the beach, carry them to your ship and bring them back safely to America."

Hathaway broke in again. "It's just like the way O'Reilly got away, except this time it will be by organized plan. It will be easy!"

"Easy?" Anthony shook his head. But in spite of himself he was becoming interested in this whole wild adventure. "I'll admit it sounds barely possible—and also downright illegal."

"Captain, you are wrong!" Devoy exploded. "These men are not criminals. All they have done is fight for freedom. Do you call your Revolutionary War heroes criminals? Washington? John Paul Jones? No, these men are patriots. They fought for freedom—and that freedom was taken away from them by force. Now they are entitled to win that freedom back. Captain, this is a God-given opportunity to right a great wrong, to rescue six human beings from the same tyranny your own country rebelled against in '76."

Anthony sat silent, his head slightly bowed.

"If it is a matter of money . . ." Devoy resumed. But Anthony waved the suggestion off with a motion of his hand. "If it is a matter of money, I repeat, you will be well recompensed. I promise to pay to you and to every man of your crew whatever the average cargo of the top seven whaling ships voyaging out of New Bedford the same time as you do will fetch. And I will pay you and your officers a handsome bonus too."

Anthony spoke slowly: "I'm sure you will be generous. And I will not deny that a profit from a successful voyage would be welcome. I see merit in your venture. I think someone should undertake it. I think it is barely possible that your plan might succeed. Mind you, I'm not saying it will. But whether I am the man—to take the law into my own hands—which is what you ask—I don't know . . ." His voice trailed off.

"Don't make a hasty decision, Captain," Devoy cautioned. "But please do not discuss this with anyone save those in this room. Not even your wife. We always fear some informer will warn the English. Thousands of Irishmen have contributed to our fund, and we will have to solicit more. Even so, only a few know the details of our plan. I trust every one of them, yet I still fear. Should we fail, the English will be forevermore on guard. There will never be another chance to rescue these men. Let me set a time limit of tomorrow night, in this room, for your decision. And I shall pray to God that it will be 'yes.' "

Captain Anthony's elbows were on his knees, his chin in his hands. The heavy breathing of Devoy and the crackle of the wood in the stove were the only sounds in the room.

Finally Richardson spoke. "George, I said I wouldn't try to make up your mind for you. I know how much you love Emmie and Sophie. But I urge you to go. I think this plan has a good chance of success. I have promised to advance Mr. Devoy and the Clan three thousand dollars toward purchase of a vessel, provided you are the Captain. She will sail with my house-flag at her masthead. As for Emmie and Sophie, you know we will look after them."

Captain Anthony got slowly to his feet. He struck a lucifer and ignited the twin wicks of the whale-oil lamp, turned the wicks up full. The sudden brightness chased the shadows from every corner of the office.

"Mr. Devoy," he said, "I see no more need of darkness here. You have spoken from your heart. I have held back because of the place my wife holds in mine. I do not want to break my vow to her, for her trust in me is priceless. But if you say I am the man to make this attempt, then I shall break my word to her and give you my pledge instead. There is no need to wait. Here is my hand."

Devoy grabbed his hand in both of his. "Captain, I thank you from the bottom of my soul."

"Good boy, George." Hathaway slapped his friend on the back. "I told Mr. Devoy you would do it. Now all we have to do is buy a ship!"

4 . The Catalpa

The night was star-bright, the moon almost down. Captain George Anthony scarcely felt the chill as he thought over the strange events of the evening. There'd never be a whaling voyage out of New Bedford like this one. And work! There'd be a devil of a lot of it before ever a sail was hoisted outbound. A whaler laid up idle and for sale could be a mighty big risk. You had to sail a ship to get the feel of her and find out what the storms and the smashing seas had done to her. The vessel bought, she'd have to be repaired, caulked, sheathed. There'd be rigging to overhaul and patch or replace. Masts to be inspected, maybe unstepped, replaced. New sails to be cut and bent. Stores to be bought and stowed. And a crew! And officers! Especially a first mate.

There was Sam Smith, in Edgartown on Martha's Vineyard. It would be worth a trip over to the island to talk to him. Maybe he'd want to go to sea again. There'd be no better first mate than he. His footsteps rang on his frosty walk. Then he stopped. Emmie! Enthusiasm for the venture oozed out of him like oil from a leaky cask. Maybe, though, Emmie wouldn't be too surprised after all. Maybe she saw how he was fretting away inwardly at being anchored ashore to a dull job at the Works. Paperwork was all right for the poor swab who had ink for blood, but if you had salt water in your veins . . .

He squared his shoulders and took the last few steps to the kitchen door. Emmie wouldn't be the only "whaling widow" in New Bedford. The hardest job would be to keep the real reason for the voyage a secret from her, but he could do that too.

As he tiptoed around in the warmth of the kitchen hanging up his cap and peajacket and taking off his shoes, Emmie's sleepy voice came from upstairs: "Sophie's asleep, George. Don't wake her. I was sleepy too. I'm sorry I didn't wait up."

He crept quietly upstairs and began to undress in the chill darkness.

Emmie asked, in a voice that carried no thought of an answer: "What did Father want, George?"

"Nothing—just—well, he wanted to know something . . . Whaling stores and such. I'll tell you about it tomorrow . . . sometime."

He slid beneath the blankets against Emmie's warm body. Her arms reached for him. He held her close to him. Fool! Fool! he thought, to let yourself be argued into taking a ship! Your place is here, in your wife's arms, with your baby nearby. There are other captains. What made you think you could do the job better than any other captain in New Bedford? Devoy could have got someone else. But you wanted to go to sea, and this is only an excuse to feel a deck under you again. You promised, never a-whaling. So this isn't whaling, it's a blow for freedom. Freedom to live and to love. But you can't tell Emmie that. You can't tell anybody that. All you can do is tell her you're breaking your promise— and breaking her heart . . .

George Anthony lay still, wide awake, counting the strokes of the town clock until the black sky grayed.

There was no widow's walk atop his house, George Anthony mused, as he looked back to wave to Emmie on his way to work the next morning, his heavy secret still locked in his troubled heart. In the bustle of her household chores Emmie had quite forgotten to ask again about the visit to her father's store.

Maybe it was better that way. Too many "whaling widows" had become widows indeed while they watched from rooftop walkways for ships that never came back.

That Emmie would object to his going never entered his mind. New Bedford, Nantucket, Martha's Vineyard women were brought up from babyhood with the understanding that love came in small moments sandwiched between long years of waiting.

The morning air was raw with portent of storm. And storm it did by nightfall—a roaring easterly that started with snow, then changed to slashing rain. For three days the storm raged, then, by nightfall of the third day, with a rise of the mercury, the whole coast from Point Judith to Cape Ann was swallowed up in thick fog.

Clearing would certainly follow the fog. George realized he could not long delay quitting his job at the Works to get about looking for a ship with Henry Hathaway and his father-in-law.

The fog searched out every cranny, shrouded the ships in the harbor, muffled the beat of the horses' hoofs on the granite-paved streets, haloed the street lamps in yellow and muted alike the clanging bells in the channel and the hour bell in the town clock. It was a night for sad things. George set about breaking the news to Emmie.

Sophie had been nursed and put to sleep in her cradle. Emmie had wrapped herself in a challis robe that clung to the soft lines of her body and lay open at the neck, half revealing, half concealing the roundness of her breasts. She and George sat together in silence as the fire on the hearth died down to glowing embers. George poked dismally at the coals. Try as he would, he could not find the words.

Emmie spoke first. "What's troubling you, George?"

"Nothing. Not a thing . . ."

"There is something. I know."

He could not speak.

Emmie moved from her chair to his footstool and laid her head on his knees. "You're going whaling again, aren't you?" she said suddenly.

"How did you know?"

"I'm not blind, George. I know how you've fretted, cooped up in the Works all day. I can see how you look to the sky in the morning as soon as you step out the door, and to the harbor as soon as you come to the corner. That night at Father's store, that was about a voyage, wasn't it?"

George nodded, running his fingers desperately through her hair.

She raised her face to his. "When do you sail?"

"We have to find a ship first. I'll have to quit the Works. This is sort of a different whaling voyage. Your father knows more about it than I do. He's the agent. We're going to look for a ship right away—tomorrow, now this storm's blown itself out."

"And you're in command?"

He nodded.

"Well, I should think you would be," she said. "How long will you be gone?" Her hands tensed as she waited for his answer.

"Two years, maybe. We'll outfit for that. Maybe not that long. We might just have luck."

Emmie's heart shrank. Two years! So many whaling wives had no more than half a dozen to share with their mates in a lifetime.

He took her into his arms. His words came choked. "Emmie, I don't want to leave you. This is a chance to have my own ship again and to do almost anything I want with her. I've got to go. This will be the last, I promise. The last voyage . . . ever. I mean it . . ."

She kissed him, slowly, tenderly. "It's all right, George. I want it this way."

George Anthony, Henry Hathaway and John Richardson set out the next morning to see what bottoms were available in New Bedford port. They disposed of the *Jeanette* quickly. Her sails were old and rotten, her rigging in need of complete replacement. Her price was high and her planks were bad. "Wouldn't get to Nantucket 'thout manning the pumps all the way," Henry scoffed.

The *Sea Gull* was a beauty, with near-clipper lines and speed written in every plank of her sleek hull. But though she was sound as Uncle Sam's dollar, she didn't look the part of the lumbering American whaleship they needed.

George gave notice at the Works. The three made plans to look further along the coast the following week.

On Saturday afternoon, Devoy arrived unexpectedly from Boston, where, he reported, he had been summoned by John Boyle O'Reilly. The editor, nosing around the docks, had come on a bark in active service that was for sale. O'Reilly was wildly excited, Devoy said, in such a hurry to pack him off to New Bedford to summon them that Devoy hadn't had a chance to see the bark himself. O'Reilly was demanding that they all come to Boston at once.

Monday morning they all arrived at the Boston depot at South and Kneeland Streets at 9:45 A.M. As they alighted, a tall, mustached man in his early thirties rushed up. He threw his arms around Hathaway's shoulders. "Henry, my true friend!" he almost shouted. Then he wheeled and grabbed Devoy's hand. "John!" he bubbled excitedly. "I've been to see it again! I know it's our ship!"

As he spoke the word, his olive complexion turned a shade pale. He clapped his hand over his mouth and spun sharply around to scan the throng on the station platform with his great dark eyes. Relieved that he saw no one to arouse his suspicions, he turned back to Devoy. In a stage whisper he went on: "She's a beauty, John! Just what we want! She's the answer to our prayers! She's . . . but, gentlemen all, I'm sorry, forgive me for going on so."

"I told you the O'Reilly was like this," John Devoy said good-humoredly.

O'Reilly hung his head sheepishly.

"We forgive you, Boyle," Devoy continued. "Now, let me introduce . . ."

O'Reilly made a bow from the waist.

In his sonorous orator's voice, he said: "I am deeply honored to meet you, Mr. Richardson, and you, Captain. So much have I heard about you from our mutual friend, Mr. Hathaway, I feel we are old friends already."

O'Reilly took a few impatient steps to start them along. "We waste time. Valuable time. You must see our ship!"

"Captain Anthony and Mr. Richardson and Mr. Hathaway must decide whether she's the right one," Devoy admonished.

O'Reilly piloted them to the street, where they hailed a cab and set out over the rough cobbles of Atlantic Avenue. They skirted the vast area which had been the scene of the Great Boston Fire of 1873. Most of the tons of blackened rubble had been carted away to fill in the marshes around the city, and new fire-proof buildings of granite and of brick were rising from the ruins. Great carts carrying stone, bricks and cement rumbled through the teeming streets. The spring air resounded with the noise of construction.

They left the cab at the East Boston Ferry slip and within fifteen minutes were in East Boston. Then it was only a short walk, as O'Reilly led them, to a wharf where longshoremen were unloading a sturdy, three-masted merchantman. O'Reilly gazed with rapture at the bark, her tall masts silhouetted against the bright March sky.

"There she is!" he said, his voice bursting with pride. "I prowled the quays for days and then—there she was. The *Catalpa!* Isn't she grand?"

"Well, she looks like a whaler," Richardson said.

"She is a whaler," O'Reilly insisted. "At least she was until her last voyage, when she was made over as a merchantman to pick up logwood in the West Indies. She's 202 tons, ninety feet long, has a width of twenty-five feet and draws twelve feet of water. I've talked to some of her officers—oh, I was very, very careful," he added with a nod to Devoy. "They said she is sound as a nut, though a bit slow."

"We won't need speed," Captain Anthony said. "It would be a mighty poor Royal Navy ship that couldn't sail rings around any whaler. Let's get aboard and look her over inside. That's what counts."

They shouldered their way up the gangplank past the stream of longshoremen, cleared themselves with the officer on duty, and went below. The ship was roomy, with a large uncluttered open hold. In the stern was a fore and aft cabin which, Richardson pointed out, could be remodeled into officers' quarters. A steerage or lazarette for food storage, and a sail locker could be partitioned off directly forward of the cabin. There would be plenty of room for oil casks between that point and the forecastle bulkhead in the bow. The forecastle itself was large for a whaler. While Devoy and O'Reilly watched anxiously, the New Bedford men poked at her timbers, looked to her planking, scanned the steps of her great masts.

Back on deck, the three experts examined rigging, masts, spars, sails, steering gear. Then, without a word, they headed back over the gangplank. The two Irishmen trailed them, O'Reilly in a cloud of dejection over their seeming lack of enthusiasm for his find.

Anthony walked slowly along the wharf for the length of the bark, Richardson pacing with him. They looked closely to her planking down to the wavelets lapping at her coppered bottom, peered intently at her standing rigging, at her great bowsprit, her heavy, square stern. Then Anthony went aboard once more. Those on the dock watched him in animated conversation with one of her officers.

When he finally came down the gangplank, silently joined the others and stolidly eyed the ship, O'Reilly could stand the strain no longer.

"Captain, please," he pleaded. "What do you think?"

Captain Anthony pursed his lips and gave the bark one more look from stem to stern, from water line to royals.

Turning to Richardson, he said, "Could do with new sails."

Richardson said, "Needs new running rigging."

O'Reilly's face grew longer than ever.

Richardson said, "Looks sound."

Anthony nodded. "Seen better. Seen worse. Officer says she's cranky as hell. Got to keep topsails on her all the time, else she'll roll over and swamp."

O'Reilly shifted nervously from one foot to the other.

"Think we can make a whaler out of her again?" Richardson asked.

"Reckon so," Anthony clipped.

"You mean she's all right?" O'Reilly demanded breathlessly.

"If you can buy her at a decent price."

"That we'll leave to you, Mr. Richardson," Devoy said. "You know what she's worth better than we do."

"A grand celebration we'll have," O'Reilly exulted. "And I know just the place for it. The ale is the finest in Boston—and I'm sure we can get something a bit more solid for our constitutions if we wish."

After ferrying back to Boston they walked up State Street, then on to Brattle Street, where they fetched up at a small public house, not far from the Pilot Office on Washington Street, outside the path of the Great Fire.

"It is a safe place," O'Reilly announced. "Timmie Sullivan, who runs it, is a Clan-na-Gael man."

Richardson hesitated at the door. "By your leave, Mr. O'Reilly— and Mr. Devoy—I think I'll just skip the celebration and get to dickering for the *Catalpa*. You say you want speed, and we like the ship. There's no sense wasting time and maybe having someone else grab her. I'll hunt up her agent and see what kind of a bargain I can drive. Wish me luck."

"That we do, Mr. Richardson," O'Reilly said.

Richardson walked quickly away. The rest entered the tavern. A red-faced man with a nose that some unkindly fist had sprawled all over his face rushed around the end of the mahogany and bowed low. O'Reilly put out his hand and the barkeep shook it most respectfully.

"Timmie," the editor said. "We want your private room in back."

"Yours, Mr. O'Reilly, now or any time at all. You do me great honor."

He led the way to a battered door leading to a tiny room, furnished with a single round pine table and a half dozen whittled armchairs.

O'Reilly motioned the others to be seated. To the barkeep he said: "Now, Timmie Sullivan, get you to your tap and draw us four mugs of your finest ale. Be honest, man, and draw ale and not froth, for our throats are as dry as dust, though it is fresh spring and there is no dust at all without."

Sullivan was back in a minute with the ale. O'Reilly lifted his mug. "Gentlemen," he said. "To Ireland!" He looked at Captain Anthony quizzically, a half-grin on his olive-tan face.

Anthony grinned back. "I'll go along with that."

"Timmie," O'Reilly ordered, as the mugs were drained. "Four more and then I don't want to see your disreputable face again until I shout for a sight of it. And we don't want anyone else to see us either. This is a meeting that has to do with the freedom of Ireland! Do I make myself clear?"

"The freedom of Ireland—in my own pub!" Timmie walked out as on a cloud, closing the door softly behind him.

O'Reilly checked the latch, then faced the others. His smile faded as he picked up his mug.

"A toast, gentlemen," he said gravely. "To what we have done this day!"

"And to what we shall do henceforth!" Devoy added.

Captain Anthony drained his ale and set the mug down deliberately. "Now," he said. "There is the heart of the matter that puzzles me deeply."

"If there are questions you would ask, fire away, Captain. John Boyle O'Reilly himself will answer your queries to the best of his humble ability." O'Reilly bowed. "Your question, Captain?"

"Why are you so dead sure you will be able to do what you plan? Why are you so sure you can get your men out of an English prison and spirited somewhere that I can reach with a whaleboat? If your people are lodged in cells behind walls . . ."

"That's our problem, not yours," O'Reilly said. "But I can ease your apprehension. Remember, I was there. The prisoners, except when they are being punished, work from sun-up to dark, gardening or repair work or loading lumber. Some go on details building roads or cutting trees in the great forests."

"Roads?" Anthony asked. "Can't prisoners escape by them?"

"You can't escape through the 'back door' of the Colony. Believe me, I know." O'Reilly took a deep draught of ale. "Cannot escape . . ." he mused, half to himself. Suddenly he yanked up the sleeves of his coat. "Look!"

On his wrists were great white scars.

"Look!" he said again, and drew up the legs of his trousers. On his ankles were more scars.

Anthony stared in horror. Even on mutineers who had been months in irons at sea he had never seen such brands.

"Those are the marks of English fetters, Captain. My souvenirs of the 'back door.'" He readjusted his trousers and cuffs. "The English have a quaint fashion of trussing up their helpless enemies. Those scars are the result of my attempts to flee into the bush country. I got the first of them when I was on a timber detail, deep in the forest. It was noontime and blazing hot. The guards were as drowsy as the prisoners. The air was heavy. You could hear the rustle of millions of flying and crawling things.

"I watched my chance. Then like a red Indian I slipped into the bush. I had no idea where to go, only to get away from my accursed English jailors. Five days later, two native trackers found me. After those five days in the heat without food, with little water, I almost welcomed the filthy wretches. They brought me back to the camp. There I was chained, wrist to wrist, ankle to ankle, and ankles to wrists. They propped me against a tree. I got bread, a dram of water. Then they took me back to prison and a dungeon.

"Captain, I thought I was quite a hand at escaping from tight spots. I had got away from Dartmoor in England, which took some doing, for I made clothes from sheets and I hid a night and a day in icy ditches waist deep in water before I made my way to a road—and right into the hands of an informer. But that was as nothing compared to the horrors of the bush. I tried six more times to escape at Fremantle. Each time my route was by the 'back door' into the bush and desert. Each time the trackers got me. Then I made the eighth try . . ."

"And that was by the sea?" Captain Anthony said thoughtfully.

"Yes, Captain, by the 'front door'—the sea. But don't think that was easy. You don't just jump off the nearest quay and swim to the nearest ship. Not in those waters. If the Water Police don't grab you, the sharks will. No, Captain, you must have friends, ashore and at sea. That's where I was lucky. First I had a powerful friend on shore—Father Patrick McCabe—and a tremendous team at sea—Captain Gifford, Henry Hathaway here, and the *Gazelle*."

"This Father McCabe . . . is he in the plan?"

"He is. Just as he was when I escaped. Henry has told you about that, but I doubt he told you what happened before the *Gazelle* picked me up."

"Can't recollect he did."

"Father McCabe's parish includes not only Fremantle itself but all the coast from Perth to Bunbury. He and I became fast friends soon after I reached the penal colony in 1868. He was always sympathetic when I told him of my escape plans. He warned me it was impossible to escape in the bush country. After that seventh try, after I had come out from my dungeon, I told the good father I would try once more, but I would not be caught again. I would end my life rather than that.

"He laid his hand on my shoulder. 'My son,' he said, in that soft voice of his, 'that is a mortal sin. Think of your soul! Wait, my son, wait. Let me think. Let me plan.'

"I did wait. I grew more and more despondent. Then one day a stranger—he said his name was McGuire—sidled up to me on the dock where I was working. He told me Father McCabe had asked him to arrange with one of the Yankee whaling captains expected in Bunbury in February—it was then December—to secrete me aboard.

"Two desperate months went by. I was sure I was forsaken. Then I heard three whalers had put in at Bunbury. I determined to flee the prison and sneak the more than a hundred miles there to try to get aboard one of these ships. But on the very day I planned this move, McGuire came to me again and said he had arranged for me to be taken off by the whaler *Vigilant*, Captain Baker, of New Bedford."

"Knew him well," Anthony grunted. "Never thought much of him."

"You anticipate my story, Captain," O'Reilly said with a smile. "I had been assigned to a timber party by then and that night I hid in the woods. Toward midnight I heard 'St. Patrick's Day' whistled. McGuire was there. We crept back along the road to a spot where he had two horses tethered. We rode hard all night, then hid in a marsh by the sea. We rode again the next night, and hid by day. Darkness came again and we rode to a place where McGuire had hidden a rowboat. In the late afternoon we saw the white sails of the *Vigilant*. We launched the boat and rowed desperately toward her, making frantic signals, but she sailed on."

Anthony nodded. "That Baker!"

"McGuire left me to try to make arrangements with another captain. But I was desperate. Alone I launched the boat and rowed all day, looking for the sail of a whaler. I saw the *Vigilant* again, but she paid me no heed. I rowed all night and in the morning I found myself back on the sands of Cape Geographe where I had started. I crept back into the sandhills and slept. I ate wild berries. I drank brackish water. Five days went by. Then McGuire returned. He had gone all the way back to Fremantle, where he saw Father McCabe again. The good father paid ten pounds of his own money—money that really belonged to the Church—to a Yankee captain who had put in at Fremantle. The captain promised he would watch out for us. Again we rowed to sea. This time Captain Gifford spotted us and picked me up—and I saw the last of Australia forever."

O'Reilly lived again the moment of his escape. He breathed deeply, then relaxed.

"You have heard from Father McCabe since?" Captain Anthony asked.

Devoy answered. "We have. He has forwarded messages from our men—at great risk to himself. He has indicated he will give all his support to any feasible plan we have to get the men out. Through him we have heard from Martin Hogan and from James Wilson direct. Wilson is always ready with ideas—as you will find out. He has, in fact, offered a plan of his own, but we think ours is better."

"Do your men know what you propose?"

"Not yet. We have purposely allowed them to remain in the dark until we have everything set up," Devoy said. "All we say to them, through Father McCabe, is not to lose hope—that we are working for them and have not forgotten them. When our shore party reaches Australia, that will be time enough."

Captain Anthony shook his head slowly.

"Does anything trouble you?" Devoy asked.

"It seems to me that a great deal of this whole venture depends on your shore party."

"On the contrary, your voyage is paramount to success."

"My part is easy, a straight navigation job. I can put a whaler in any port you name at any time you say."

"Of that we are certain. And we are just as certain that our shore party can put our men on the beach waiting for you. Never fear, Captain, we will get our men out. I pledge it."

Anthony spoke again. "Now if we get the *Catalpa*, always supposing we do get her——"

O'Reilly interrupted him. "Of course we'll get the bark. The *Catalpa* is ours, you can wager on it."

"I hope you're right," said Anthony. "You've found us a good ship. When we get her, I'll have to have her refitted and overhauled. That will take some time."

"How long?" Devoy asked.

"Depends on her condition. Can't say till we see her bottom."

"A month?" Devoy prodded.

"Be crowding things . . . I just can't guess."

"We want to get you under way as soon as possible," Devoy insisted.

"I won't waste time. So when the *Catalpa* is ready, what then?"

"Sail just like any whaler and hunt whales—at least for the first part of your voyage. We want you to speak with other ships, play the part of the wandering whaler. And we want you to ship home what oil you take, just as you normally would."

"Then I'll sail for the Western Grounds, and ship from Fayal. That's the usual procedure."

"Splendid."

"When do you want me in Australian waters?"

"Early next year. By late February or early March."

"Then I should start from the Azores in late fall of this year. By that time the bottom will be foul and the ship will be slower. I can't risk careening her for scraping. I'll need the sailing time."

"I'm sure all will go well," O'Reilly said. "And now, I can do with some food. Gentlemen?"

Before the day's end, Richardson had struck a bargain with the *Catalpa*'s owners. The price was $5,250. He advanced $4,000 of his own cash on a thirty-day personal note given by Devoy. On Saturday, March 13, 1875, papers were signed and the *Catalpa* belonged, nominally, to J. T. Richardson, agent.

5 . "Greasy Voyage!"

Clear of her logwood cargo, the *Catalpa* lay at her East Boston wharf with only a caretaker aboard, waiting for her new owners to take possession.

Both Anthony and Richardson determined it would be better to do the job of overhaul in New Bedford, rather than in Boston. They could trust local workmen—more than could be said for craftsmen in the big city—and supervise repairs if the job were done in the home port. George and his father-in-law arranged for a tow, and at noon two days after she had been sold, the *Catalpa* was under way at the end of a hawser, headed for Boston Light and the open sea.

Their course took them east of, but within sight of the hook of Cape Cod, off Provincetown. It was dark when they spotted the flash of Highland Light. Nauset, Chatham and Monomoy lights beckoned them on through the night. At dawn the tow captain took a westerly course through Nantucket Sound. With Nantucket and Martha's Vineyard to port, the tug brought the *Catalpa* into Buzzard's Bay by way of the ferry channel between Woods Hole and Nonamesset Island. They fetched City Wharf in New Bedford in the late afternoon and made fast.

Early the next morning, Captain Anthony engaged John W. Howland, New Bedford's best ship's carpenter, to direct the bark's overhaul. Anthony had decided views on the work—views that, to Howland's mind, were widely at variance with normal practice in remodeling a merchantman into a whaler.

For one thing, complained the carpenter, the captain, in planning quarters for officers and men, was cramping his stowage.

66

"You give the men so much room, George, where in tophet you goin' to stow your ile?"

Anthony was firm, silently planning quarters for at least six extra men—and maybe three or four more of the land party—on the return voyage. "When can you finish her, John?" he asked.

"Well, lessee now . . . heavin' down, caulkin', sheathin', riggin', masts, spars, new boats, sails, cabin, hold . . ." Howland ran over the items rapidly. "This is March 16. Give me good weather, no complications, make it about the end o' May or the first o' June."

Captain Anthony shook his head. "You got to do better than that, John. I want her out of this port in six weeks!"

" 'Tain't possible!"

"Put more men on. Push them. Get the sailmakers on the job today. Order the small boats built. Get riggers here . . ."

Howland scratched his gray head. "A body would think you was goin' a-piratin', way you want this here ship rushed outa port."

"I'm not going pirating, John, you can lay your bottom dollar on that."

Next morning Howland had a swarm of workmen on the *Catalpa*. The masts were stripped of their yards and rigging, then royal masts, topgallant masts and topmasts were sent down. Only the three masts themselves—fore, main and mizzen—rose stark and stubby from the deck.

The bark was towed to shallows and hove down by chains and heavy tackle so that her starboard side, clear down to her keel, was exposed at low water. Anthony himself inspected the bottom with Howland, saw it was sound—and sighed in relief. Caulkers stripped off her old sheathing, repaired some planks, pounded fresh oakum into her seams and nailed on bright new copper sheathing. Then the port side was similarly gone over. Two of the Captain's allotted six weeks were gone before the ship was tied up once more at City Wharf.

Busy as he was with details of ordering supplies for the voyage, Anthony spent many hours aboard her, "gettin' in the way," as Howland growled.

One noontime, shortly after the bark had been tied up again

at the wharf, Howland came up the aft ladder with a long face. "I got bad news, George," he said. "The riding keelson under the mainmast is bad rotted. Wonder we didn't pull the mainmast right outa her when we hove down. It'll take a coupla extra weeks to fix."

"You just can't have extra weeks."

John Howland came up with a solution unique in the business of wooden ship repairs. He made a new oaken mainmast riding keelson, eased off the ratlines, main chains, after shrouds, mainstay and preventer stays at the maintop. Then, with heavy tackle erected on stout shears, he hoisted the ponderous mast sufficiently for his men to take out the rotted step and slide in the new. It took five days.

With repairs booming along, Captain Anthony set about rounding up his officers. Richardson, as agent, took on the task of signing the crew—Kanakas, Malays, Bravas, a few New Bedford boys, some farm lads from "down East" eager for adventure—but no English subjects.

When Devoy had given him the *Catalpa* to command, George Anthony had made up his mind that the man he wanted as his first officer was the lad he grew up with in sail, Samuel P. Smith of Edgartown on Martha's Vineyard. At twenty-nine Sam was a rugged, two-fisted sailor, sandy-haired, round-faced, just back from a two-year voyage. If it was humanly possible to coax him to sign on again so soon after he had come ashore, Anthony determined to do it. He took the ferry that called at the Vineyard.

Sam wasn't home when George knocked on the door of the salt-stained shingle cottage where the Smith family lived. Sam's mother allowed her son probably was down to Lucas Coffin's wharf, and George set course for the waterfront again. He found Sam painting a skiff bright red.

Sam stood off to admire his handiwork, then turned slowly to acknowledge George's greeting. He wiped the paint splotches off his hand and grasped George's palm in his. "I know why you're here. I know what you're up to."

George winced. "What do you mean, Sam?"

"I heard you had a bark. The *Catalpa*, ain't she?"

"What else you hear?"

"Goin' whalin', ain't you?"

George breathed an inward sigh of relief. "Sort of figured on some."

"And you come over here to see if I'd ship with you?"

"Sort of had that in mind."

"Well, git it outa your mind. I aim to stay ashore a mighty good long spell."

George shrugged. "Everyone to his taste, like the lady said when she kissed the cow."

"*Catalpa* ain't so much." Sam paused. "Who you shipping aft?"

"Antone Farnham as second officer."

"Good Brava. Good man with a dart. Pretty old."

"Forty-three, but a stout man in a whaleboat."

"Who else?"

"George Bolles for third mate."

"Young un. Got plenty sand. Bit wild, maybe."

"He'll do—with you to boss him. What do you say, Sam? First officer."

"Told you no, George."

"Why not? Give me one real good reason."

Sam's face turned red. "Got a girl. Thinkin' I'll get married some day."

"Who'd want an old salt cod like you? What are you going to live on?"

"Thinkin' of doin' a little fishin'. Got a chance to buy a good schooner with Lucus Coffin here. Catch us some cod, halibut and such."

"Grown man like you fooling with bait!"

"Money in it. Gotta have money to get married," Sam said thoughtfully.

"You can make a damn sight more in one good whaling voyage than you can in ten years of fishing, and you know it."

"And be gone a couple year and get nothin' too."

"I know we'll get a full hold of oil. You'll get a top lay from the oil and the spermaceti. And the ambergris too, if we're that lucky. But more than that, I'll see you get a whopping bonus on the side. You'll need money to fix up this girl of yours in a nice house. Do I know her?"

"Cap'n Nate Jernegan's daughter," Sam said proudly.

"Lottie Jernegan! Lottie's a nice girl——"

"'Tain't Lottie," Sam said in almost a whisper. "Amy Chase."

"Isn't that robbing the cradle? Amy Chase isn't more than fourteen."

"Well, we sorta got an understandin'. You should hear her play the pie-anna."

"Why don't you give Amy Chase a chance to grow up? I'll bet she still plays with dolls. Two years from now, when you get back from our voyage, she'll be past sixteen. And then you can court her honorable-like, and marry her too, and Captain Nate and his good wife won't object at all. Two years a-whaling and you'll come home ready to take out your own ship."

"First officer?" Sam said shrewdly.

"Right!"

"Bonus?"

"Right—and a big one too. Amy's pretty eyes will pop out of her head when you spill all the gold in her lap."

"When you sailin'?"

"John Howland says he'll have the *Catalpa* ready by the end of April. We got some good boatsteerers lined up already. Bob Ranacker . . ."

"Ain't he sort of sickly?"

"The sea air will do his cough good. What do you say, Sam?"

Sam took his paint brush and gave a touch to a spot he had missed. He put the brush back in the paint pot. He kicked the beach pebbles. Then he stuck out his horny hand. "Put 'er there, George. You talked me inta it. I never wanted to go shore fishin' nohow. I'll ferry over one of these days soon . . . after I talk to Amy."

Captain Anthony took the ferry back to the mainland with a light heart. As his first in command he had a man he could trust, a man who could handle the ship in any emergency, a man who could bring the ship back home safe in case things went wrong in the rescue attempt. He rubbed his hands in satisfaction.

April's end was fast nearing. The decks and the holds of the *Catalpa* boiled with activity. Aft the foremast a copper camboose was built which, filled with water, would protect the deck from charring when the tryworks, built of bricks above it, were fired to boil oil. Masons bricked in huge copper kettles with a hearth beneath. Above these trypots rose a shelter so that boiling could be done in the rain. Another shelter covered the aft ladder, the galley and the wheel.

The oversized oak davits Captain Anthony insisted on were bolted in place. New whaleboats glistened in fresh white paint. Spare spars were stowed on deck and below. Standing rigging was tarred, new running rigging reeved through blocks, new sails bent.

As the painters took over, stores arrived hourly. Into the holds went everything the crew would need for the two-year voyage: 2,400 casks either whole or in knockdown form, thousands of iron hoops, 19 cords of firewood, 135 barrels of beef preserved in salt-peter brine, 100 barrels of salt pork, 90 barrels of hard bread baked, at Anthony's direction, in Watson's Bakery in New Bedford, 70 barrels of packed flour, 1,100 gallons of good Cuban molasses, two huge boxes of loaf sugar, 1,000 pounds of dried apples, 100 bushels of potatoes, 1,000 pounds of butter, 1,000 pounds of lard, 700 pounds of dried codfish, 300 hickory smoked hams, rice, dried beans and dried peas, cornmeal, salt, spices, coffee, tea, chocolate, tobacco. Pens were built on deck for hens and pigs to be used for fresh meat in the early part of the voyage.

There was a complete set of carpenter's tools, four big grind-stones, six muskets, six revolvers, powder, ball, cartridges, nails, rivets, needles, thread, sailmakers' palms, lanterns, pots, pans, spiders, tar, rosin, tinware, crockery, copperware, blacksmith tools, iron in rods and bars, lumber to repair boats, paint, cordage in all necessary sizes, spare sails and spars, thousands of fathoms

71

of harpoon line, tubs for lines, knives, hatchets, harpoons, lances, cutting spades, iron hooks, buckets, extra harpoon and lance shafts, waif flags to mark killed whales, stationery supplies, prints and ginghams for possible trading with natives—and a Bible.

In the medicine chest were simple remedies: boneset, pennyroyal, fennel, tansy and other herb teas, elixir of vitriol, opium, tincture of laudanum, spirits of camphor, spirits of nitre, blue pills, Atwood's Bitters, salts, castor oil, salves, opedildoc, bicarbonate of soda, sulfur candles and other fumigants, bandages, splints, a sharp knife, tweezers and forceps. Twenty gallons of good Medford rum, two gallons of Holland gin, five gallons of brandy and two gallons of port wine went into the captain's private "lazareet," the whaler's name for storage rooms below deck.

The *Catalpa*, ready for sea, cost the Clan-na-Gael committee exactly $18,000.

On Monday, April 26, Richardson telegraphed John Devoy: "*Catalpa* ready. Sail on your order." Devoy arrived in New Bedford the next morning, and inspected the bark. Departure was set for Thursday, with the tide.

John Boyle O'Reilly, Devoy told Anthony, had decided not to come down to New Bedford to see the *Catalpa* off. Still fearful that informers might link the whaler with a plot to rescue the Fenians should he be at the wharf, he had elected to stay in Boston. He had entrusted his farewell message to Devoy—a slip of paper with the words: "Go gcuiridh Dia an t-a'dh ort, Captain Anthony. Go soirbhi' Dia dhuit." And the bold signature: "John Boyle O'Reilly."

Anthony gave the paper back to Devoy, saying, "Now I *am* puzzled." He smiled. "Will you read it to me, Mr. Devoy?"

Devoy crossed himself. "It says in Gaelic: 'May God send luck to you, Captain Anthony. May God prosper you.'"

Anthony bowed his head. "Tell Mr. O'Reilly I thank him from the depths of my heart."

The night of Wednesday, April 28, Captain Anthony and Devoy met again in John Richardson's office. This time the whale-oil lamp burned brightly.

"There still is need for secrecy, of course," Devoy said with a smile, as Anthony commented on the bright light. "We are always fearful, Captain. You have kept your promise manfully so far. Now I beg of you, keep the secret of the *Catalpa's* mission locked in your heart . . ."

"Until?" Anthony questioned.

"Until there is no longer any possibility of her real purpose getting to the English. The sad history of Irish plans is that there has always been someone to blurt out the secret just for the sake of seeming important, or selling his soul for mean profit. We are still gathering funds to pay off the debt on the ship and the expenses of our shore party. Thousands of Irishmen know something is in the wind. Yet so few of us know the actual details that I am confident the English either will not learn of them, or, if they do, will be so complacent in the supposed security of their prison that they will call it 'just another silly Irish plot.' "

"There is one man I shall have to tell," Anthony said slowly. "My first mate, Sam Smith. I must let him in on the plot. He will have to be in charge of the ship while I am ashore to pick up your men."

"Tell him then—by all means—but not until you are almost at your goal. Now, I think we should have a complete understanding of what we expect of you, and what you should expect of us in the Clan-na-Gael. You know your immediate goal, of course?"

"To put to sea like a whaler, act like a whaler, take what whales I can—like a whaler."

"Right. And ship your oil from Fayal in the Azores in late summer or early fall, just as you would on a regular voyage."

"And when I have shipped my oil?"

"Then set course directly for West Australia. We want you to arrive in Bunbury, the seaport south of Fremantle, in February or early March, 1876—next year."

"And there?"

"Now you should know something more about our shore party and their plans. We are sending two men to Australia this autumn. From New York will go John J. Breslin, the man who liberated our chief organizer for the Republic, James Stephens, from prison in Dublin. He knows English prisons. He knows the English mind. There is a price on his head, of course, and if he is caught in Australia—or in any British port for that matter—he will end his days in the very prison from which he intends to rescue our men."

"He sounds like a brave man."

"Brave and resourceful, too. You will never be disappointed in John Breslin. Now, when he reaches San Francisco on his way to Australia he will be joined by another Irish patriot still to be chosen by our friends on the West Coast. The two will proceed by fast steamer to Australia. Since our winter is summer in Australia, they will have good weather to spy out the land, get in contact with the prisoners and perfect their plans. They will pose as strangers aboard ship and on arrival in Australia. They will communicate with each other only in utmost secrecy or by code messages.

"They will go by assumed names. Mr. Breslin will call himself 'Collins.' His aide will be instructed to call himself 'Johnson.' Remember those names."

Captain Anthony repeated the aliases.

"Now, we will expect you to bring the *Catalpa* to Bunbury at the time set. Meantime our two men will have everything in readiness for the escape. When you get to Bunbury, anchor, go ashore and register the arrival of your ship with the proper authorities. Then get in touch with Mr. Breslin."

"That is a vague order, Mr. Devoy."

Devoy shook his head, smiling mysteriously. "I have here," and he took out a penned manuscript, "a set of code messages that I'm sure will cover every situation that arises. Guard this code, Captain, it is vital to our venture. Mr. Breslin will have the only other copy."

Captain Anthony took the papers and stowed them in an inner pocket. "They will go directly into my ship's strongbox."

Devoy rubbed his hands. "Well, Captain, I think we have covered about everything. I am going to say farewell to you now.

I will be on the dock when you sail, but I shall remain in the background. I do not want to run any final risk right at the moment of your sailing. So, Captain, good luck, good winds, God bless you, and may the Holy Virgin protect you and bring you back safely with our men." He took Anthony's hand and shook it firmly.

"Thank you," Captain Anthony said gravely. "I promise you, if your men on shore do their share, I'll land your party at the Battery in New York City."

A sharp shower dashed over New Bedford before dawn Thursday. The thrumming of the wind in taut rigging and the splatter of rain on the deck woke First Mate Sam Smith from the uneasy sleep of his first night in the tiny portside cabin he would call his home for the voyage. The *Catalpa* rocked uneasily at her mooring lines and bumped at the chafing gear hung between her fresh-painted hull and the dock timbers. He groped for an oilskin and slipped it over his shoulders before climbing the aft companionway. Under the shelter of the housing he looked to the bark's shore lines. In the eerie light of false dawn the yards and furled sails were wrapped in a gray haze. Even as he looked, the rain stopped and the clouds began to break toward the east. All secure, he went below.

The moan of the wind and the dash of rain against the window-pane woke Emmie Anthony from the sleep she had thought would never come. She stirred, and George came half awake. His hand sought her and his fingers came away moist from the tear that had trickled down her cheek.

"Don't cry," he murmured.

"I didn't mean to, George. I just . . ."

"It won't be long. I'll be tied up at City Wharf again before you know it," he said as he stroked her hair.

His weatherwise ears caught the noise of wind and rain. "Showering?" He was out of bed in an instant and looking out the window. "Won't amount to much, breaking to eastward."

Then he was back in the warm bed, his arms holding Emmie tight.

Dawn brought a bright sky flecked with tiny lacy clouds. The sunlight gleamed on the brick and the granite of the whaling capital, washed April-clean.

From his window in the hotel halfway up the hill on which New Bedford was built, John Devoy looked out on the sparkling, rain-drenched, rolling meadows bordering the town. Seaward, harbor waves danced behind a lattice of shining, tall masts and bright white spars, spidery shrouds and the gray-white furled sails of dark-hulled ships. The shower, the brilliant dawn and now the bright spring green grass and trees made Devoy's hopes soar. It was an omen indeed, an omen of success. It was as if the whole world were bathed in the glorious emerald of Ireland.

Shortly after seven o'clock, a light wagon rattled over the cobbles of Front Street and jolted to a stop at the gangplank. A sweating clerk for Richardson jumped from the driver's seat and rushed aboard the bark. To his hail Sam Smith, Antone Farnham and George Bolles turned out on deck. With a couple of crew members they hustled to the wagon and hauled the last of the *Catalpa*'s crew over the wharf planks and up the gangplank to dump them into the forecastle, paying no heed to the drunken sailors' grumbling at this rude end to their last night's carouse.

At the stroke of ten from the town clock, John and Sophia Wrisley Richardson drove up to the Anthony house in the family surrey. Emmie brought out Sophie, bundled in white wool. George came out with his spyglass and chronometer in hand and closed and locked the door. He climbed into the carriage behind Emmie and gave her the big brass key.

"I won't be needing this for a while," he said with a faint smile.

John Richardson reached over to George and took the telescope from his hands. With a smile he said: "You won't need this any more!" He picked up a parcel from the carriage floor. "Here's a new one and a powerful sight stronger than the one you had.

Should be able to spot," and he paused for a split second and winked covertly, "whales lots more miles off!"

"Take care of the old one, Emmie," George said, "you'll need it when we're sailing into port again."

The dock was jammed with relatives, friends and well-wishers, gathered to shout the traditional "Short voyage and a greasy one!" that sent the whaleman on his way. Out of the corner of his eye George spotted Devoy standing quietly aloof at the extreme seaward end of the dock. Devoy gave no sign of recognition. Neither did the Captain.

The family stood bound by an awkward silence. Richardson took his son-in-law's hand. "Good luck, my boy. A profitable voyage—and may you succeed in everything you set out to do. God bless you and bring you back safe to us."

Mrs. Richardson kissed him. He took little Sophie in his strong hands, swung her aloft and held her at arm's length. "You'll be running to meet me, day I get back," he said, as he swung her down again and kissed her nose, then handed her to her grandmother.

George swept Emmie into his arms. She snugged her head against the heavy cloth of his pea jacket. "Good-by, George. Take care of yourself."

George tilted her face up, kissed her ardently, then broke away suddenly. In a few strides he was on the deck of the bark.

A tug chuffed alongside the *Catalpa*. Under the direction of Harbor Pilot Will Nickerson, lines were made fast from the tug's bow and stern.

A crewman ran up the bark's red-bordered, white houseflag with "J.T.R." in bold black letters. Emmie's heart felt a bitter pride as she saw the Richardson emblem whip to the breeze from the mainroyal mast—bitterness that her own father had been the one to make George break his vow never to go to sea again, perverse pride that her man was in command of a ship again, just as she knew in her heart he wanted to be.

Now to the peak of the foremast went the bark's burgee, a big blue "C" on white. From the spanker flaunted the Stars and

Stripes. A string of bright signal flags snapped between fore and main and main and mizzen masts.

Pilot Nickerson stood by Captain Anthony on the afterdeck. The helmsman gripped the wheel spokes.

"Ready with your shore lines, Captain," Nickerson warned.

"Ready bow and stern lines, Mr. Smith!"

"Bow and stern lines manned, sir."

"Ahoy the tug!" Nickerson yelled. "Get her under way!"

The towboat's propeller churned white water. The towing hawsers drew taut.

"Let go bow line, Captain," Nickerson directed.

"Let go bow line," Anthony ordered. A dock hand threw the line off the dock dolphin.

The bark's nose swung away from the dock.

"Loose stern line!"

The sailor on the line let his line pay out slowly from its three turns about the deck bit. The *Catalpa* moved slowly, ponderously seaward.

"Now give him slack," Anthony called.

The sailor slipped one turn off the bit. The stern line sagged in the water.

"Let go stern line!"

A dock hand slipped the stern line off the wharf dolphin. The *Catalpa* was free of her shore fetters. Captain Anthony stood at the rail. He waved to his family and to his friends, then threw a kiss as Emmie held Sophie up. The gap between ship and shore widened.

Devoy stood on the end of the dock. As they passed, he gave a quick touch of his fingers to his hat. Anthony gravely returned his salute, then turned to his First Mate. "I reckon we got enough breeze to drop the tug directly we get her well down harbor," he said. "That is if Mr. Nickerson agrees."

The pilot nodded.

"Get some of our people aloft! I'll want fore and main tops'ls, main t'gallant, gaff tops'l, stays'l, flying jib and spanker."

Ashore the crowd drifted away. The Richardsons, Emmie and the baby went back to their carriage.

Long after the wharf had been deserted by all but the screaming, diving, complaining gulls, John Devoy stood, collar of his ulster turned up, watching the craft that carried his greatest hopes. As she dwindled in the distance she seemed frail, whereas nearby she had seemed stout and sturdy. Devoy sat on a bundle of cask staves and kept his eyes on the fast fading bark until he no longer could make out the forms of those on board. His mind raced the thousands of watery miles to the six men in Australia, and he held his rosary and murmured a prayer. Finally, the *Catalpa* was a dot in the distance. He rose slowly from his perch, his legs stiff in the early spring chill. He picked his way shoreward along the splintery-planked wharf, with its gull-fouled piles, its jumble of casks and cask staves, rusting iron hoops, oaken harpoon shafts, frayed cordage and stacks of greasy galley firewood that had "been a-whalin'" before.

Pools of oily rainwater glistened in all the colors of the rainbow. Over all, mingled in the fresh spring air was the fatty reek of whale oil, the stench of tar and dead fish, the mustiness of rotting wood and the salty tang of the sea.

His feet touched the cobbles of busy Front Street. He gave one last look back. The *Catalpa* was out of sight.

To work now. There was so much more to be done.

6 . First Take

The white sails of the pilot boat blurred into the afternoon haze. Under the *Catalpa*'s bluff forefoot, the Atlantic swells bore the whaler up and up as if she were in the palm of some sea monster's paw, then let her slide, hissing, down into their oily troughs. The dark water burbled past her waist to trail bubbly-milky-white astern where a few gulls screamed their strident "ha-ha-ha-haah-haah." Whitecaps began to fleck the water. As the afternoon wore on, the sky turned to the dirty gray that foretold rain and squalls.

Captain Anthony stood easily at the side of his helmsman, watching the leach of the main topsail.

"How does she handle?" he asked.

"She do good, sair," the Malay wheelman replied. "She pay off. I got hard time keepin' she full!"

The Captain nodded shortly. The ship seemed alert enough as she heeled to the wind. Her bow dug purposefully into the waves, throwing icy spray over the forward deck.

The Captain strode from the shelter of the decked-over wheel-house to the weather quarter and leaned against the rail. He took a deep breath of the salt air. Astern, No Man's Land and Martha's Vineyard were blue-gray blurs slashed with the dun-yellow of beach sand where land and water met. He looked long at the fading land. This would be Emmie's first night as a whaling widow. How would it be with her? And how was it with him? To be truthful with himself, tired as he was, he began to feel pride that he was the one, of all New England's captains, who had been chosen. Devoy could have had his pick of them, not only in New

Bedford, but in New London and Fairhaven, in Duxbury and Provincetown, in Scituate, Marblehead, Edgartown, Nantucket— wherever that hardy breed called whalemen fretted "between voyages." And many a one with more years at sea than George Smith Anthony could boast.

But—and for this he was proud indeed—he knew he could keep his mouth shut, and some could not, for drink had a way of loosening a tongue. And that was the real reason why he stood on the weather quarter of the *Catalpa* this momentous April day.

He turned his back to the rising sea and watched the business of getting the bark shipshape for the long voyage ahead. The men cleaning the deck of shore-side refuse were in the charge of Second Mate Farnham, dark and lean with the far-seeing eyes of his seafaring race. Farnham clipped his commands sharply.

In the bow, some sodden wretches, half sick from their night's merriment before sailing, struggled to lash down the two bow anchors under the sarcastic orders of First Mate Smith.

"Mr. Smith!" Captain Anthony called sharply. "All hands, Mr. Smith! Let's see what dockside scum we got that calls themselves seamen."

Smith cupped hands to mouth and shouted: "ALL HANDS!"

A boatsteerer picked up the cry below. "ALL HANDS!" echoed through the bark.

The men below stumbled up the forecastle ladder—whites, Malays, Bravas, Kanakas—bleary-eyed, dirty and whiskery.

"Line up on th' lee rail!" the First Mate shouted.

Shivering in the raw wind after the warmth of the forecastle, the men shambled into a line. They were joined by the anchor crew and the men who had been swabbing the deck. Only the man at the wheel held his post.

Captain Anthony looked them over keenly. "You seem short-handed, Mr. Smith. We shipped more men than this. Have some gone overside already, gut-scared of a real whaler?"

"They's some more below, sir!" Smith said.

Captain Anthony's voice rose a peg. "Mr. Smith, I said 'All hands!' and I mean 'All hands!' " His eyes darkened and his heavy brows knit together. His voice rose another peg. "When I give an order on this whaleship, I want every man jack to jump. And I want you, Mr. Smith, and you, Mr. Farnham, and you, Mr. Bolles—" he pointed a stabbing finger at each in turn—"to jump faster than anyone. Now!" His voice rose to a commanding shout: "ALL HANDS, MR. SMITH!"

Sam gulped. Farnham and Bolles stood stockstill.

The First Mate shrugged his shoulders imperceptibly. Wasn't goin' to be much brotherly love on this voyage, that was for sure. Well, that's the way it was, that's the way it would be.

"Aye, sir!" Sam clipped the words short and snapped to the Third Mate. "Mr. Bolles, take Mopsy and Gingy and lay below!"

Bolles and the two Malays ducked down the forward companionway and into the forecastle. Inside three seamen lay in a welter of broken bottles, unstowed seachests, scattered dunnage.

The scant illumination from the forecastle deadlight prism showed matted hair, livid faces and red, swollen necks. Their clothing was wet and slime-filthy, and they snored with the drunken heaviness of cheap dockside rum.

"Him much drunk!" Gingy said.

"Him goddam much drunk," Bolles mocked. "Him all three really goddam much drunk."

The two Malays shoved and hauled the three onto deck like mealsacks.

Captain Anthony spurred one of the inert forms with the solid toe of his boot. "And who are these able-bodied seamen, Mr. Smith?"

Mopsy rolled the three face up. Smith touched each in turn with the toe of his boot. "This black one is Robert Ceil, he's a St. Helena islander. This one is John Coeking, he's from New Britain. And this one is Cyrus Hill, he's from New Hampshire."

"All right, Mr. Smith. The introductions are over. Now slosh them down and stand them up so we can get a good look at men who couldn't answer a command." The Captain leaned dispassionately against the weather rail.

"Mr. Bolles!" Smith ordered. "See to it!"

Under Bolles' direction Mopsy and Gingy dipped buckets of icy water from overside and drenched the three. Again they drew the buckets inboard, and sloshed the icy contents on the men. A third deluge did the job. The three crawled to their feet, sputtering, gagging, cursing.

"Belay that jabberin'," the First Mate warned. "Line up with the rest."

"Belay hell!" Hill whipped the sea water from his black hair with his fingers. His dark face twisted in rage, his brown eyes looked almost as black as his hair. "I'll say what I goddam please any time I want to. I got my rights. No man livin' kin slosh sea water on me. No man alive can make me shut up——"

The First Mate's right fist shot out and caught Hill flush on the point of the jaw. The seaman crashed to the deck. As he went down, Captain Anthony studiously eyed the set of the sails.

Hill wobbled to his feet, shook his head, rubbed his jaw. Smith unconcernedly stepped to one side.

Captain Anthony strode in front of Hill. "So you have your rights, have you, Hill? All men have rights. But they are rights guaranteed under the law. I am the law on this ship. If you obey the law on this ship—and that means me—you'll have all the rights you can use, I promise you."

He walked along the ragged line, throwing back his broad shoulders and fastening his gray eyes on each man in turn. Then he strode to the center of the line and faced his men, rocking a little on his heels as he began the traditional speech of a whaling captain at the start of a voyage.

"Now get this into your thick heads. This is a whaler," he snapped. "I am the Captain. Remember that, every mother's son of you. When you get an order, you jump out of your hide to obey it.

"That goes aboard ship and in her boats. We have good officers. Mr. Smith, Mr. Farnham and Mr. Bolles know how to chase whales and kill them. We have good boatsteerers. And I have a word for you boatsteerers too. When you dart that whale, you bury that iron in her hump. Harpoons cost money. Good hemp line costs money. I don't want any wasted. And when your officer goes forrard to lance and he wants blackskin on his boat, then you put him right atop that whale, so's he can churn his lance. I want no chicken-livered men working for me. Taking whales is mighty serious and mighty dangerous. You can get in a hell of a mess if one man in a boat shows the white feather. You know that as well as I do. I don't mind competition atween boats, but when the time comes for everyone to lay together, so help me, if any man don't pull his weight, then, by God, I'll break him.

"And now here's another thing. We've got plenty of good food in our lazareet. We've got plenty of fresh water. But that doesn't mean food nor water can be wasted. If I catch any one of you wasting grub or taking more than his share of water, he'll go on hardbread and water for a month. And, by God, I'll dock the rations of his watch, too. I want no griping about the grub. It's the same as you'll get on any whaler out of New Bedford. It may not be fancy, but it'll stick to your ribs.

"You were shipped because you're all supposed to be old hands. Some of you don't look dry behind the ears yet, so I'll soon find out if you're lying. If you are, there'll be no watch below until you know the ropes.

"You, man at the wheel! Your course is south by east. Hold it. I'll have my eye on the compass day and night. You let her yaw off I'll know it and you can bet you'll know it before I get through with you.

"If you're square with me, I'll be square with you.

"Mr. Smith, you and the rest of the officers pick your watches. Tomorrow you can pick boat crews."

Captain Anthony turned smartly on his heels. Without another look at the men he walked to the aft ladder, took one last glance at the sails and disappeared below deck.

The voyage of the *Catalpa* had begun.

At sun-up the next day Captain Anthony set about making the *Catalpa* ready for the "serious and dangerous" business of chasing and killing whales.

"All hands" were called as soon as the cook had slapped morning meal on pannikins and hot coffee in mugs, and the men had polished it off.

The business of selecting boat crews was far more important on a whaler than the choosing of watches. A good boat crew meant the difference between killing a whale and losing valuable gear. Richardson had signed up four of New Bedford's best boatsteerers. These, with the officers, were the backbone of each boat crew. The Captain's choice for his steerer was Antone Ferris, a Cape Verde islander from New Bedford. He was past fifty, the oldest man in the *Catalpa's* crew. His gray hair shocked over a swarthy skin and piercing black eyes. He was big for a Cape Verde man— five feet eight inches.

First Officer Smith had Bob Ranacker as his boatsteerer, despite the racking cough that often doubled him up. Ranacker was just twenty-two, black-haired, black-eyed.

Second Officer Farnham chose thirty-year-old John Rosso of New Bedford for his steerer. Rosso had a bit more education than most of the islanders in the crew; he could write his own name and was proud to sign the ship's articles "Rosso" and not just set his "X" against "Malay"—the agent's donation toward last names when the native jargon got too complicated to translate into English.

Third Mate Bolles picked the Yankee from New Britain, Connecticut—John Coeking—whom he had sloshed with sea water at the Captain's orders. Coeking, at twenty-seven, was a runt among the men, a bare five foot three, with bright blue eyes.

Boatsteerers stood beside officers as the rest of the boat crews were chosen, offering suggestions, objections, approvals as the men lined up.

Captain Anthony stuck to his secret decision to have none but Malays or Kanakas in his boat. His choice of Mopsy Rosso, Gingy Malay, Tom Kanaka and Zampa Malay brought an almost imperceptible raise of an eyebrow from Sam Smith.

Smith's crew included Caleb Cushing, from Harwich, Massachusetts; Tom Knipe, a St. Helena islander; Joe Rosmond, from Saint Lucia in the West Indies; and Mike Malay.

Farnham picked Henry Paine, a blond, seventeen-year-old,

Woodstock, Vermont, lad who already had been on two voyages; Lumbard Malay; Henry Parrott, another St. Helena islander; and Dennis Duggan, red-headed and about thirty-five, vaguely "from Pennsylvania."

Third Officer Bolles had almost a solid Yankee crew in his boat: Hill, the defiant New Hampshire lad; Edmund Gleason, a swarthy thirty-year-old from Candia, New Hampshire; Walter Sanford, nineteen-year-old six-footer from Raynham, Massachusetts; and as his only black boy, Bob Ceil, a St. Helena islander just turned eighteen.

The bark was under easy canvas, making good her south by east course from her last landfall as the boat crews made ready for the task ahead. Every man in the crew turned to, with the exception of the man at the wheel. The thirty-foot-long, six-foot-beam whaleboats—the *Catalpa* carried four instead of the five customary on a bark her size—were checked from stem to stern, then loaded with the equipment necessary for the taking of whales. Snugly stowed were lantern kegs, with tight-sealed contents of lantern, matches, candles and hardtack; water kegs, bailing buckets, mast and leg of mutton sail; darts, lances—these sharpened to razor edge by the mates themselves, boat spades, waifs or identification flags to put on the carcass of a dead whale that might have to be abandoned for the time being after the kill; oars, including the twenty-three-foot-long steering oar the boatsteerer would handle when the mate went forward to give the lancing death thrust into the whale's foot-in-diameter jugular; hatchets and knives to slash fouled lines.

Hundreds of fathoms of two-and-a-quarter circumference manila harpoon line fresh from the ropewalks at Plymouth were left-handed coiled, then trailed in the ship's white-frothed wake to take out kinks, stretched taut, then recoiled into the line tubs—three hundred fathoms to a tub, two tubs to a whaleboat. But the tubs, unlike the rest of the gear, were stowed on deck, waiting for the first cry of "Ah . . . *blows!*"

The welcome shout was not long in coming.

By Tuesday, May 4, with good whaling grounds near, the

Catalpa ghosted along under her two lower topsails and a head sail. Lookouts were posted in rings high atop the foremast and mainmast.

"Five pounds of tobacco to the first man who raises a whale!" Captain Anthony promised.

At ten of the morning, down from the foremast ring came the cry: "Ah . . . *blooows!*"

A convulsion of excitement swept the deck.

Until that moment all had been quiet, the slatting of canvas and the creak of rigging the only sounds. From dawn to dusk when a bark was on the whaling grounds, it was a hard and fast rule that no unnecessary sound should be made. Seamen cat-footed in bare feet. Officers' orders were hushed.

The very slightest sound, magnified a thousand times through the water, startles or "gallies" a sperm whale. Although his ear is but a quarter of an inch across, for all his tremendous tonnage, the sperm is equipped with the best hearing of anything that swims or walks.

"Ah . . . *blooows!*" the lookout called again.

Captain Anthony rushed for the mainmast shrouds and started aloft. Just as he yelled, "Where away?" Caleb Cushing, on the articles as cooper, popped out of the forecastle hatch, hammer in hand. He headed aft toward the tryworks, lost his balance when the bark rolled to a sea, plunged headlong on deck, walloped one of the two four-barrel trypots with the hammer as if he were clouting the biggest gong in a Chinese temple, and fetched up in a bloody-nosed heap at the foot of the workbench abaft the tryworks, bringing most of the bench, with its overburden of cutting spades, lances, harpoons and other ironware about him in a crashing heap.

From the lookout came the wail: "Thar she go flukes!" as the whale dived for the bottom of the sea.

Captain Anthony swung angrily to deck. " 'Fore God, Cushing, you clumsy fool, another break like that and I'll clap you in irons for the rest of the voyage!"

Bad luck rode high in the royal yards next day too. Once more the lookouts saw the fine white spray that told of sperm whales. Another spout and another. A whole school of sperm to windward! Captain Anthony crowded on all sail to head them off so that boats could be lowered. But a heavy wind and rain squall forced him to take in canvas.

Two days of bad luck in a row gave the still-rankling Hill a chance to blow off to the watch below in the steaming forecastle. The icy bath he'd got on the first day out had not faded from Hill's memory; in fact, the more he thought about it, the more he seethed. Hill was a rugged New Englander who spoke his piece and be damned to what anyone else thought. Dark enough to pass for a Brava, he aspired to be cock of the roost over such as the runty Coeking—as blond as Hill was dark—and the black-haired Ceil.

Hill sounded off loud about Captain Anthony and his ability that night the *Catalpa* had sighted the pod of whales. "You seen it, mates. You seen it, all of you. He ain't no whaleman. He sailed this bark right acrost their slick. I seen it, plain's day. You seen it too. He gallied them whales. We'd gotten some of them if'n he hadn't. You can't sail no ship acrost a sparm's slick and not scare the hell out of 'em."

Coeking, one of those who had the watch, nodded emphatically. But sandy-haired Caleb Cushing, despite his bawling out by the Captain, came to the skipper's defense.

"Cap'n ain't to fault," he said. "I scared hell out of the first whale we saw. I admit it. I was a clumsy ox. I bin t' sea afore, bin a-whalin' afore. What the hell does a hayseed like you know about skippers or whales?"

"I bin t' sea afore," Hill said heatedly. "I ain't no hayseed. You kin ask anyone here. I'm right, ain't I?" He looked defiantly around the seamen, sprawled on "haystacks" or on seachests.

Cushing finally admitted Hill had a point. Sailing over a whale's slick was poor seamanship and it sure had worked out bad for them this day.

For a whole day rain slashed the sea and the hungry wind whistled through the rigging. Only the two lower topsails and a headsail were spread. It was useless to keep a lookout posted in the mast rings. The keenest eyes in the world could never have seen the spout of a sperm in that welter of gale-driven whitecaps.

The morning of May 6 the gale abated and a gentle breeze set in. No more canvas was sent up, however, for with the whitecaps vanishing, it was time to slog slowly along and watch for whales. The *Catalpa* made but two or three knots. Lookouts went aloft again that day: Antone Ferris climbed to the foremast rings; Henry Parrott took the mainmast.

For almost two hours after sun-up their eyes swept the watery waste. As the bark rolled first to starboard, then lazily to port, their perches a hundred feet up in the masts swung in dizzying arcs as if they were the bobs on giant pendulums that had suddenly gone mad and were swinging upside down.

It lacked a few minutes of six when their watch would end. No eyes could take more punishment than two hours of intense watching. Parrott gave one final look about the horizon. His tired eyes spotted something. It might be a distant whitecap. Then again . . . He looked again. Yes, it must be . . .

"Ah . . . *bloooows!*" he yelled.

First Mate Smith was on deck. He leaped for the mainmast shrouds, hoisted himself over the futtocks and clambered up to the rings. He threw a knee over the main topgallant yard and yelled at Parrott: "Where away?"

Parrott pointed excitedly. "T' labbad, sar. Thar!"

Smith saw the spout as he followed the pointing finger. Just then Ferris sang out from his foremast perch: "Ah . . . *blows!* 'Bout a mile ahead o' he!"

Captain Anthony was still buttoning his pants as he hit the deck. "What do you say, Mr. Smith?" he called.

"Two sparm, sir! Just lazin' along!"

"How far?"

"About five miles, sir."

The Captain called to Bolles, standing by. "All hands, Mr. Bolles! We got work to do!"

"*All hands!*" Bolles yelled, running to the fore ladder to screech down into the forecastle.

Now the lookouts could see the two whales plainly. The ship

crept up on them. One of the whales was large, the other much smaller. The lookout watched the bigger of the two. "Thar's 'e ol' hump . . . thar's 'e ol' hump . . . thar's 'e ol' hump . . ." Parrott called as the whale swam in porpoise-like loops.

Suddenly: "Thar 'e go flukes!"

The whale sounded, its gigantic tail flukes slapping the water and sending a tremendous shower of white water about. The second whale dove at almost the same instant.

All hands waited, almost breathlessly. Captain Anthony said softly, as if afraid the whale might by some miracle overhear: "Mr. Smith, go alow. You and Mr. Bolles get them. Ready your boats . . ." He raised his voice. "Mr. Bolles, ready your boat."

The bark ghosted along to the slap of canvas and the faint squeaking of blocks and rigging. If the whales had been gallied, the bigger one would stay down for a long time—a minute to each foot of length for a full-grown sperm. That could mean an hour for the big one, which appeared about sixty feet long.

If the whale had not been alarmed. . . .

The tremendous bulk roared to the surface in a slather of foam, heaved clear of the waves a scant two miles ahead of the bark, then dropped back in a cloud of spray, with a splash such as only sixty tons of living meat could make. Nearby, the smaller whale also surfaced and blew a smoking, snorting mist through its spout. Needlessly Parrott shouted: "Thar 'e whitewaters!"

Oblivious to the whaleship, the two whales sported playfully. Parrott kept up a running commentary as the boat crews raced to get ready for lowering.

"Thar 'e pitchpoles!"

The larger of the great beasts stood on his tail, his enormous boxlike head and half his length completely out of water.

The boat crews formed up alongside each whaleboat swinging from the davits at the bulwarks. Oars, harpoons, lances, knives, lantern kegs, water casks—all were checked hurriedly but carefully by the officers.

"Steady, now," Captain Anthony ordered the helmsman. "Steady as you go. You boatsteerers, when you get alongside, no misses. I want oil. Steady . . . steady . . ."

"Thar 'e go lobtail!" shrieked Parrott as the large whale reversed his tactics and stood on his head, waving giant flukes clear of the waves. The smaller swam in circles as the big one put on his show.

"Mr. Farnham," Captain Anthony called. "Ready to brace round the yards. We don't want to run this bark atop of them."

"Thar's 'e ol' hump . . ." Parrott kept track again of the porpoise-like leaps in which the whale now indulged.

"Now . . . Mr. Farnham . . . main topsail aback!"

The thud of bare feet on the deck planks was almost simultaneous with the creaking of the great yards.

The big sail eased around.

"Main tops'l aback, sir!"

"Helm up, you at the wheel. More . . . bit more . . ."

The ship came up into the wind.

Captain Anthony jumped to the deck. The whales were a scant half mile away. Every man in the crew, every officer, was as tense as hunters stalking a deer.

"Ready boats!"

The ship lay almost motionless in the water, the backed main topsail balancing the drawing fore topsail.

"Hoist and swing!"

The two whaleboats were swung over the side.

"Lower away!"

The boats hit the water almost at the same moment. The crewmen slid down the grip falls.

"Over tubs!"

The tubs of harpoon line were lowered to the waiting arms of the boat crews.

"Mr. Smith, take the big one. Mr. Bolles, take the little feller. Ready? Out oars . . . good luck." Captain Anthony waved the boats off.

Once in the water, none of those in the boats could see their prey. Smith, in his boat, and Bolles, in his, kept a sharp eye on the signals the captain ran up on the bark. A hauled-up weather clew on the fore topgallant sail meant "sail more to windward"; a hauled-up lee clew, "sail more to leeward"; dropped colors on the maintruck, "whales have sounded"; colors up, "whales have breached again."

After an hour's hand-blistering row, the *Catalpa* signaled that the whales were still to windward. Doggedly the men pulled at the heavy oars. Again and again the signals came that the whales had sounded or had breached. At least the hunters knew that their quarry had not been alarmed.

In Smith's boat, Bob Ranacker fought for breath. A coughing spell rocked his slim body. As boatsteerer he had bow oar, with harpoon at his side. His job was to dart the whale, hurling the iron so deep into the whale's fatty hump that it would not tear loose. He pulled as hard as the rest, though each stroke tore at his lungs.

Two hours went by. Suddenly the whales breached within sight of the men, the first time since the chase began that they had actually sighted their prey. Both whales were swimming lazily on the surface.

"He's ours, boys!" Sam Smith urged. "Pull, lads. Just a bit more and we're on top of him. Ready, Bob, ready with that dart!"

Ranacker drew a deep breath. He shipped his heavy oar and crawled to his place in the bow, resting his knee against the "clumsy cleat" for balance. He took up the harpoon and ran his eye along the line that carried from its sharp iron head to the stern line tub.

"Pull, boys, pull!" Smith urged. The oars bent as the boat flew through the water. His keen eyes sensed rather than actually saw a great black mass streaking upward. "Stand by your iron!" he warned Ranacker.

Suddenly, dead ahead, an enormous, mossy, barnacled mass twice the length of the boat heaved out of water. There was a hoarse whistle as the whale spouted. The rank, moist, pent-up vapor blew damply over the boat and men. Waves sloshed at the huge blunt head. Vast whitish patches of sea-lice specked the whale's sides. The broad back was a glistening jet-black. The great sides rippled. The flukes of the tail, twenty feet in width, fanned the air.

Trained to their task, none of the boat's crew save Smith and Ranacker actually watched the whale. They waited as tensely for their orders from the First Mate as Ranacker did for his.

"'Vast heavin'! . . . Ready . . . Bob . . . ready . . ."

The boat slid noiselessly up almost to the side of the whale. Ranacker arched his back.

"Give it to him!" Smith yelled.

Ranacker heaved. The dart sank three feet into the whale's hump.

The great beast shuddered, as if wondering what to do.

"Peak oars! Watch that line!" Smith warned.

The whale came to monstrous life. A deafening *whoosh* as the mammal felt the harpoon was followed by a sobbing intake of air as the whale drew breath and sounded.

A sudden jerk sent the unprepared into a shin-bruised heap in the bottom of the boat. For an instant the bow went completely under water as the whale took off. White water cascaded into the boat.

"Bail! Bail, you bastards!" Smith shouted.

He scrambled forward, ready to give the whale the death thrust of the sharp lance—the mate's privilege. Ranacker scrambled aft to grab the steering oar. A paroxysm of coughing shook his body and blood trickled from his lips, but he paid it no heed. The line smoked around the loggerhead bit.

"Get outa th' way o' that line, goddam you lubbers!" the mate yelled. "Dump some water on it. You want it to catch afire?"

The whaleboat churned at express-train speed with water pouring over the bow and the gunwales and slashing the full length of it. The crew, drenched to the skin, bailed frantically. The bow rose slowly. The harpoon line writhed and squirmed from tub to loggerhead, from loggerhead to chocks. The hemp whistled and smoked, screamed and rumbled. Still the quivering boat flew through the water, building up a sudsy wake.

On the *Catalpa* Captain Anthony watched the boats through his glass. To his disgust he saw Bolles iron his whale, then watched him slash the line with a hatchet, probably because the hemp

93

had snarled. A new iron gone. And God knew how much line.

In Smith's boat, however, the stern tub was empty and the waist tub half gone before the whale slowed in his first dash. For a minute the line ceased to run through the chocks. The boat slacked its forward course.

"Stand by to haul line!" Smith ordered.

Inch by inch, foot by foot, fathom by fathom the line was retrieved and coiled in the sternsheets. Half had been recovered when the whale breached, spouted, sucked in a cavern of air, then sounded again. Once more the line smoked out, and the boat scudded along on a "Nantucket sleighride." Then the pace slacked, and again the crew heaved in the line. This time the whale lay on the surface, spent with its mortal labor.

"Out oars!" Smith ordered as he stood ready with a lance griped in his sinewy hands.

"Pull, Three! Pull, Two! Pull all!" The boat crept nearer and nearer to the black, rippling hulk. " 'Vast all! . . . *Now!* Pull all!" Steady! Steady! 'Vast all!"

He bent almost double and grunted as he drove the razor-sharp lance until it brought up at the socket—a full six feet in the neck of the whale. For an instant he churned the head of the lance.

"Stern all!" he yelled. "Stern all! Lively!"

The gigantic flukes lifted clear. They hit the surface with a cannon-shot thump, flinging a fountain of water on the crew. The line smoked through the chocks. Once more the whaleboat skimmed the waves.

But the whale was rapidly weakening. When he surfaced now, as he did at shorter and shorter intervals, his spout was pink with blood. No longer did he swim with bulldog determination. He altered his course, swimming aimlessly and with greater and greater effort. Finally he lay on the surface, motionless again.

The whaleboat hauled close. Smith poised with another lance. "Put me right on him this time, Bob. Gimme blackskin on this yere boat!"

Cautiously the crew rowed, then, at Smith's order, peaked oars. The boat slid along the body of the whale until the thin black skin that covered the foot-thick blubber scraped off on the white-painted planking.

Smith tensed, then drove in his second lance, aiming this time at the spot he knew was closest to the foot-in-diameter jugular. The lance sank deep and true. But as it dug in, and before Sam had a chance to churn, the oaken shaft snapped. In a flash Smith, cursing loudly, thrashed overboard.

The whale churned flukes, lashing right and left in death agony. The flukes caught Smith and tossed him fifty feet into the air. He squirmed, spread-eagled, then splashed into the roiled water, knocked out.

The whale began to turn over on its side. A horrid gush of clotted blood poured from its spiracle and drenched the boat crew. The great barnacled carcass turned fin-up and lay awash.

Sharks gathered from nowhere and slashed in like vultures. The sea was red with blood.

Ranacker put the whaleboat alongside the half-floating mate. Cushing grabbed the collar of Smith's shirt and yanked him from the shark-boiling water. He dragged the mate over the whaleboat gunwales. The officer's body collapsed in the bottom of the boat. His face was blue. Blood flowed from cuts on his head and neck.

In the distance the *Catalpa* boomed on with most of her canvas spread. Captain Anthony, watching the end of Smith's chase through his glasses, had seen the accident. In an hour the bark was alongside.

Smith was still breathing faintly when his crew passed his limp form up to waiting hands aboard ship.

Bolles made the whale fast to the *Catalpa*'s side. Cutting-in could wait.

7. Mutiny

They carried Smith across the silent deck into the First Mate's tiny cabin, and laid him on his bunk.

Captain Anthony and Gingy peeled off the First Mate's sodden clothes. A giant purple bruise covered most of his ribs. Blood still oozed from the cuts on his head and neck. He was breathing, but faintly, his face death-pale, his hands and feet clammy.

This was a hell of a way to start the voyage, George thought as he prodded the bruised side to see what was broken. Outbound scarce a week, one skinny whale—he didn't look as if he'd boil more than forty barrels, even though he was a sixty-footer—a new iron and a hundred fathoms of new line lost by that blockhead Bolles, and now Sam laid up and maybe like to die. If he did live and was badly hurt, he'd have to be transferred to the first homeward-bound ship they met. Then what? How could he trust a Brava like Farnham to handle the ship alone in Australian waters? And Bolles—his first whale and a mess of it!

Perhaps it would be better to turn back. They weren't too far from New Bedford—less than a week's sailing. Devoy wouldn't have even started talking to his shore party yet. They could get another first officer that would measure somewhere up to Sam.

His searching fingers found no splintered bones grating under the bruised flesh.

"Get some blankets," he told the Malay.

While he waited for Gingy to return, George rubbed Sam's body with opedildoc. Gingy helped wrap him in the blankets so that the camphor and castile soap ointment could soak in. The Captain mixed a mug of rum and hot water and trickled it between

Sam's lips. Sam stirred and his throat went through the motions of swallowing. George gave him more of the hot drink.

Bolles came timidly in, braving the Captain's possible wrath, to see how the First Mate was faring. He was set to work chafing Sam's feet with more of the opedildoc.

A half hour ticked by.

Bolles said: "Captain, want I should get the stage out and start cuttin' in? It's gettin' late."

Sam opened his eyes and looked about him. He started to get out of the bunk, but the Captain held him back.

"Wait, Sam, you aren't fit to get on your feet yet. You've been hurt bad. That whale's flukes gave you a hell of a going over," he said.

Sam impatiently pushed the restraining hands away. He got groggily to his feet, wincing as the muscles on his bruised side took the strain.

"Where's my dry clothes? Ain't no damn whale livin' or dead can make a calf outa me! I'll boss the cuttin'-in!"

And he climbed the companionway to the deck.

Captain Anthony shook his head. By God, now there was a man.

On the deck, all hands set to at cutting-in. The cutting stage, a rectangular framework of wood, some twenty feet long and fifteen feet wide, was run out from the starboard side of the bark, and suspended by heavy tackle over the dead whale. Two huge blocks were hung from the maintop. From them hung heavy hempen tackle attached to four-foot-long wrought-iron blubber hooks.

Smith took his place on the outer plank of the stage, with Farnham and Bolles on the sides. With razor-edged cutting spades, attached to twenty-foot long wood shafts, they sliced two holes about four feet apart in the foot-thick blubber. A crewman clambered down on the slippery carcass and rove a chain through. One blubber hook was attached to the chain and crewmen put a strain on the tackle. The mates began cutting through the blubber to the pinkish flesh beneath. The tough, fatty mass began to peel off the carcass. Leviathan's body revolved slowly as the blubber strip came off much like the peel of an orange. Only an occasional slash of the spade was necessary to free it from the flesh beneath, but the spades were in constant use marking the spiral vertical cut along the edges of this first "blanket piece."

When the blanket piece reached the chock of the maintop block, two holes were made in the blubber at the cutting stage level and another chain was riven through. Then the second blubber hook was attached and the first piece was severed and swung down the main hatch into the hold.

It was dirty, greasy work—and dangerous. The sea was bloody. Sharks fought for the chunks of pink meat exposed by the blubber-peeling and turned like cannibals on each other as lance-armed crewmen slashed into their ranks.

Always the cry was "Sharp spades! More spades!" from the three on the cutting stage. A man kept a grindstone sparking as he put edges on the worn spades and fitted them back on shafts.

There was no time to light the trypots. With the coming of the dark the glass plunged and the wind rose. By the time the whale had been stripped and the guts searched in vain for any lump of the grayish, fabulously valuable ambergris a sick whale might form in its innards, the *Catalpa* was creaking and groaning under the wind. Only the "case"—the whale's giant head—remained to be salvaged.

A blubber hook was fastened in the head and the vertebra in the neck severed. The fifteen tons dead weight of the case canted the bark until the outer edge of the cutting stage was far under water and the waves rushed into the scuppers. The head was swung inboard and securely snugged on deck. The cutting stage was run in just in time; the full force of the gale hit as night closed in.

For two days the *Catalpa* rolled and shuddered in the hand of a tropical storm, only a rag of her topsails showing. In the steaming hold the blubber slimed, then began to rot. A million cockroaches appeared from nowhere. The stench from the blubber penetrated everything—bunks, blankets, clothes, food. Hill had plenty of company to help him grumble in the forecastle, though he knew as well as everyone else that the condition was not un-usual in a whaler. But it was a chance for him to talk big, and he grabbed it. There had been plenty of time to boil, he orated, only the Captain was afraid to take a man-sized chance.

By the afternoon of the third day, the gale subsided enough for the trypots to be fired with wood from the galley. The boiling commenced. A hole four feet in diameter was cut into the "case." Inside lay, honeycomb-like, the pearly-white spermaceti, the stuff fine candles were made of and the most prized of all the oils a whale could yield.

Into the snowy grease clambered two Malays, naked as the day they were born. Armed with wooden bailing scoops, they bailed the spermaceti into buckets, and the buckets were carried to the trypots. There the spermaceti was hand-shredded and fed into the pots, where it was brought only to the boiling point before it was dipped out and run into cooling tanks. So precious was the stuff that during the bailing of the case all scuppers were stopped and every bit of slop from the head was scooped up and put into the pots.

Once the head was drained and dumped overboard to the ever-present swarms of sharks, the blanket pieces of reeking blubber were hoisted from the hold, cut into smaller "horse-pieces" about a foot in width and a little more than that in length, then scored with a mincing knife, the better for the oil to be tried out. The minced chunks were tossed into the trypots and the oil boiled out. The tried-out scraps were used to feed the hot flames under the great kettles. As the trypots filled, the oil was baled into cooling tanks, then run into casks in the hold.

Hour after hour the exhausting work went on. Watch relieved watch. The lurid flames from the trypots illumined yards and rigging, where the flapping of the ghostly sails added to the weird twisting of the flames. Black smoke belched from the tryworks stacks, coating rigging and sails with soot. The decks became skidways, with oil, bits of blubber, chunks of tried-out fat every-where.

Below decks, shakes of staves were unbound and casks knocked together. Iron hoops were driven on. Lukewarm oil from the cooling tanks on deck was run into casks, which were then headed and stowed.

With all the work the whale boiled but thirty barrels of oil and a scant eight of spermaceti. A barrel for each foot of length was the usual yield.

For a week pleasant weather held. The *Catalpa,* now on the whaleman's famed "Western Grounds," took two whales on May 13.

Two more weeks went by. On June 13 two more small whales were killed. Then for another full month the lookouts saw nothing from their masthead perches but the limitless sea. The weather ranged from poor to foul.

Other ships, spoken one or two a day, had luck and boasted plenty of oil. The *Sarah B. Hale,* out only two months, had ninety barrels, the *Wave* had forty and only a week out. The *Janet Gartland* boasted four hundred and fifty barrels for her eight weeks. The *Pacific's* casks held a whopping 1300 barrels and only three and a half months out.

It didn't take the gloomy predictions of Hill to remind the crew that, so far, their lay "wouldn't be wuth a-spittin' on." More and more of the forecastle hands nodded soberly to his grumblings that the *Catalpa* was a hard-luck ship driven to hell-and-gone by a know-nothing skipper. They turned their wrath on the cook, for his constant offerings of salt pork or salt beef, served up with potatoes boiled in sea water. Even the lobscouse—that weird combination of hardtack, pork grease, molasses and water—"waan't fitten t' eat." And when would they get dandy funk, that delicacy of powdered hardtack, molasses and water, baked brown? And what about some plum duff, though the concoction of flour, yeast and dried fruit might be as tough as a hunk of raw whalemeat?

In mid-August, Bob Ranacker, in spite of all the Captain could do for him, died of the ravages of consumption. The crew stood bareheaded and solemn as Anthony read the words of the burial service. The body, weighted with some worn-out cutting spades, slid into the sea.

Forward, after the service, Hill loudly declared he knew what had killed Ranacker. "'Twasn't th' consumption at all," he insisted. "It were th' rotten grub wasted poor Bob away. We got a guilty man aboard this here bark—an' it's the Captain, I sez!"

Heads nodded.

"I sez it's time to send a deputation aft an' make known that we ain't goin' to starve to death like poor Bob did!" Hill declared.

Hill picked Paine and Gleason, both fellow Yankees, for his committee. They marched determinedly from the forward deck into the forbidden midship territory reserved for the boatsteerers and the Second and Third Mates. The Captain yelled at them as they stepped down the companionway abaft the tryworks.

"Who gave you permission to step in boatsteerers' country?" he demanded. "Your place is forrard and you know it. If you got no jobs to do, I'll mighty quick see you have!"

"We demand to be heard!" Hill spoke up. "We got our rights to send a deputation aft!"

"I thought we drowned that talk out of you the first day at sea!"

"'Twas the lousy grub what done Bob Ranacker in! We demand——" Hill dropped his eyes before the Captain's glare. Paine and Gleason trembled a step or so backwards.

"Ranacker was a sick man afore he ever set foot aboard this bark. You know that as well as I do. Ranacker thought 'twould do him good to voyage a spell. I thought so too, else I wouldn't have shipped him. That the sea air did him no good, God rest his soul, is the Lord's doing and not mine. The grub on this whaler is as good as that on any ship ever sailed out of New Bedford. Now get forrard and get to work else I'll have the lot of you flogged and put in irons on bread and water for the rest of the voyage."

It was August 27 before the *Catalpa*'s darts sank home in another whale, a small one.

On September 5 the bark *Draco*, Captain Peakes, homeward bound to New Bedford, hove into view. Captain Anthony eagerly accepted the trumpeted hail of Captain Peakes that they "gam" awhile. He bundled up the letters he had written to Emmie, to his father-in-law and to Hathaway in hope he would meet just

101

such a vessel bound to New Bedford. He and Sam Smith took their boat crews over to the *Draco,* both officers standing ramrod stiff as was the custom, holding to no support on the row over the rolling seas. The first and second officers of the *Draco* boarded the *Catalpa* for their share of the gam. For a half day the visiting went on. It was like going home for Anthony, for he had served on the *Draco,* under Captain Peakes, for almost ten years.

Captain Peakes suggested that since tunny abounded in the waters near the Azores, it might be a good idea to turn out the *Catalpa*'s crew to fish for them, then swap the fresh fish for potatoes and other provisions.

But before the rugged outlines of the islands were raised by the lookout, the bark had another chance at whales. Almost incredibly, Third Mate Bolles lost two more. The last one took away a whole tub of good line. For ten minutes Bolles squirmed under a torrent of tongue-lashing from the Captain that kindled a fierce resentment in his heart.

In bad temper, the crew fished for tunny, using white rags as lures, and boated over 2,500 pounds in a few hours. Captain Anthony loaded his catch into one of the whaleboats and went ashore at Santa Cruz, on the island of Flores, to try to barter. His dicker with some natives on the town dock had just begun when a customs authority clapped him on the shoulder and announced he was under arrest. "For smuggling," he was informed. The fish, the customs man insisted, were products of American fisheries and as such were being smuggled into the island. The fish must be returned or full duty paid.

Captain Anthony turned to the native with whom he had been dealing. "Dump the damn things in the ocean," he said.

Mollified, the customs man announced that the American no longer was under arrest. The Captain returned to the *Catalpa* after paying good American dollars for the potatoes he had hoped to gain by barter. The whole episode was food for another heated session in the forecastle.

"By the old harry, I got enough of this lugger," Hill announced to the edgy men. "Catchin' tunny 'stead of whales! I'm goin' to jump ship soon's we git to Fayal. Who's with me?"

Coeking, Paine, Gleason, Cushing, Ceil, Joe Rosmond, Zempa Malay and John Rosso joined Hill. It didn't take much persuading on the part of Hill to get Third Officer Bolles in on the plot.

The *Catalpa* fought for every foot of the hundred and forty miles from Santa Cruz, on Flores, to Horta, on Fayal. Wild gales and torrential rains swept the seas. The final stretch in the treacherous Fayal channel between the islands of Fayal and Pico was a nightmare of navigation before the bark could dock at Horta.

No sooner had she dropped her lines over the dolphins than the ten mutineers leaped over the rails and raced for hideaways on shore.

Local police did their best—or said they did—but six men went uncaptured. Hill, Paine, Coeking and Bolles were caught in a waterfront dive, before they had had a chance to absorb much liquor and certainly without sight of a woman. Handcuffed, they were brought back to face the captain.

Bolles was stripped of his officer's rank and ordered to the forecastle.

"You come to your senses, and maybe I'll be easy on you," Captain Anthony said. With a six-man shortage in the crew, he had to swallow some of his wrath and put Hill, Coeking and Paine to work unloading the oil casks.

The *Catalpa* had taken only 210 barrels, worth at 31½ gallons to the barrel and 50 cents the gallon, around $3,300.

Seven new men were signed for the crew: Antoine Sylvester, Frank Perry, Manuel Antoine, Louis Tonquin, Antoine Maui, George Duguin and Joe Dutton. The Captain moved the *Catalpa* out in the harbor to prevent any more escapes.

New sails were ordered to replace those worn to rags in the wild Atlantic gales from which the bark seemed never to escape. A quantity of lumber was shipped—to repair boats, the men and the officers were told, but in reality to build accommodations for the Fenians. The Captain drew on his agent for $3,000.

There was an uneasy peace on the bark as work was pushed to get her ready for sea again, but Hill wasn't one to give up. He waited a full week, until things had quieted down. Then he and Coeking made bundles of their shore clothes and their few personal belongings, wrapped them in bits of oilskin, hid the bundles under the spare whaleboat atop the tryworks shelter, and waited for the right time to slip off ship.

Sunday night, October 25, was heavily clouded. The sea was fairly calm. In the town the yellow lights winked out, one by one.

Shortly before midnight the two slipped out of the forecastle, picked up their bundles and crept to the *Catalpa's* bow. The lone watch on deck slumbered peacefully.

Silently Hill made a rope fast to the foremast shroud, and dangled the end in the water. He and Coeking strapped their bundles on their shoulders, slipped almost noiselessly into the water, and swam strongly toward the dark distant shore. But the bundles of clothing became waterlogged despite the oilskin covering. The tide turned against them.

Coeking panicked. "I cain't make it, Cy! I'm a goner. I'm a-drownin'!" He let out a lusty "Help! Help!"

The *Catalpa's* watch on deck woke up. "*All hands!*" he bellowed. "Man overboard!"

The cry brought the Captain, Smith, Farnham and the crew tumbling out of their bunks.

Coeking was still yelling for help between gulps of sea water, but Hill kept swimming toward land.

"Mr. Smith, lower the waist boat and pick up those men!" Captain Anthony ordered.

Coeking was pathetically glad to clamber weakly aboard the whaleboat. Hill fought savagely until a clobber over the head with an oar knocked him half senseless and he was hauled aboard and dumped in a heap on the bottom.

Only an hour after their break the two were back on the *Catalpa* and Smith stood them before the Captain.

"I'll be goddamned if I'll have any more trouble from you two,"

Anthony shouted. "Mr. Smith, tie these mutinous sea-lice up until they learn who's boss on this ship."

The two men were bound by wrists and by ankles, made to squat on the floor, and a wooden pole was passed back of their knees and through the wrist bonds.

After three hours, Coeking, arms and legs and body aching, said he'd had plenty. His hands and feet were uncast from their spunyard bindings, and he went forward to work, rubbing his cramped muscles.

Hill still was in a snarling rage. "You ain't got guts enough to beat me down," he raged at the Captain. "You kin torment me till you tire out, you ain't makin' no calf outa Cyrus Hill. And you ain't makin' me work no more on this stinkin' starvation ship."

Two more hours went by. Hill's arms were freed so that he could wolf down breakfast. Then he was tied up again. All day he crouched, doubled up, the wood pole under his knees chafing the skin. At sundown he was still raging. He and Coeking were dumped in the steerage and put under guard.

The next morning, Coeking said he was sorry and was cast loose and sent forward. Hill snarled a bitter "Go to hell!" when the First Mate asked him if he was willing to apologize to the Captain. But two hours later he sang a different tune. He begged for the Captain. "You win," Hill said, with an attempt at a grin. "I'm sorry I sassed hell outa you. And I'm sorry I jumped ship."

His bonds were released. One of the crew rubbed his back and arms and legs with opedildoc. The balm soothed his smarting muscles, but didn't salve the hate in his heart, nor did it allay the kidney block that developed from his salt water immersion and his long stay in bonds. Before sundown he developed a high fever and lay moaning in his bunk.

Captain Anthony sent a whaleboat ashore to fetch a doctor. For two days it was nip and tuck whether Hill would survive. But survive he did, and the ship went back to normal routine again. Revictualing was rushed. Put aboard were more potatoes, fresh vegetables, oranges, lemons, bananas, chickens and pigs. Some of the water casks were filled, though the Captain counted on taking most of his fresh water supply on board in the Canary Islands where the water was known to be of better quality.

November 6, the *Catalpa* took her anchors and, clearing for "the River La Platte," stood for Teneriffe in the Canary Islands off the African coast—last port of call before the long voyage to West Australia, last opportunity for Sam to quit ship if he decided against sharing in the plot to free the Fenians.

All the long hours of the voyage from New Bedford, George had debated when would be the best time to tell Sam of the plan. Many an hour he had stood by the weather rail, weighing the words he might use when it came time to put the whole case before the man he most needed to see it through. Above all, he decided, it would not do to try to argue Sam into making his decision. It would be better to make a simple presentation of the facts, then let Sam make up his own mind. He couldn't blame Sam if he decided to leave ship at Teneriffe and go home. The rescue would be dirty work, dangerous work and maybe bloody work. There was no reason for a man like Sam to risk his hide in some other man's wild scheme. Now was the time for Sam to be told. He would have to weigh the risks while there was still a chance for him to leave.

A few hours out of Fayal, he called Sam to his cabin. The *Catalpa* rolled along under light working sails in a gentle southeasterly.

Sam sat uneasily on the corner of a bench. He was not used to being invited into the Captain's private quarters, even though George Anthony was his friend as well as his superior. All through the voyage he had tried his best not to presume on their long friendship. He had kept to his proper post on the lee rail and what conversation he had had with the skipper was strictly ship's business.

The Captain was all business at first. "Can we put Bolles back in his mate's berth, you think?" he asked.

"Reckon we could," Sam clipped.

"Think he's learned his lesson?"

"Reckon he has."

"Any trouble with the crew? Any more talk of jumping ship? Any one of the new men side with Hill?"

"Ain't heard nothing much. They'll all forgit it, come some whales, decent-like whales. That's been the big gripe, us not gettin' oil in our hold. Get us some big ones, the hands will come around."

There was a brief silence. Then Anthony spoke. "But suppose we don't go whaling again?" he asked.

Sam gave an involuntary start. "Not hunt more whales?"

"You thought we'd keep right on chasing sparm, eh, Sam?"

Sam looked at Captain Anthony as if the skipper had gone daft. "Well, ain't that what we set out for to do?" he managed.

"We could go places in a whaler, Sam." The Captain's voice was low. "Maybe Australia." George looked closely at his friend. If there had been any leak on the *Catalpa*'s mission, Sam's face would show it now, but his expression was one of bewilderment.

"Australia? What the hell . . ."

"Fix yourself comfortable, Sam. I've got a yarn to spin . . ."

For a half hour he told Sam the whole story. The First Mate's eyes bugged as he listened. Finally the Captain finished.

"I'm going to free those men, Sam. The bark was bought for that job and fitted out for that job. You got a right to get mad as hell at me for making a fool out of you. And you got a right to quit this ship at Teneriffe. You can easily get a berth there on a ship homeward bound. You'll get your fair lay of what oil we've taken, just as if you'd stayed with the ship. I don't want to argue your mind up for you.

"But I hope you'll stick by me, Sam, and go with me. I picked you because I figured you would. I need you as a friend and as the most trustworthy first officer a captain ever had."

Sam sat silent, his brow furrowed. Questions crowded into his mind—what would his job be in the rescue, what chance would there be of ever getting out of an English prison if they were caught, what would happen if George were arrested and he was left with the ship? His face showed the strain. Then his mind eased. If George Anthony said it was the job to do, then George Anthony was right. His face lit up. He stuck out his calloused hand and grabbed Anthony's.

"George, I'm with you. I'll stick by you in this here ship if she goes straight down to hell and burns off her jibboom!"

8 . The Shore Agents

The *Catalpa* sailed with a debt clinging like barnacles to her broad bottom. That debt was John Devoy's first concern when he walked shoreward after the bark that carried his heart's hopes had faded into the spring mist.

Devoy soon learned money was not, indeed, to be found on trees. It was in the grimy overall pockets of the hod carrier. It came from the greasy jeans of the engine hostler in the round-house. It came from the fireman in the boiler room, from the truck driver, the bricklayer, the track walker, the coachman, the gardener. It came from the very poor—the "shanty" Irish—and it came from those who were pulling themselves up by their own bootstraps and becoming known as "lace curtain" Irish.

The money came in nickels and in dimes, in greenbacks and in gold pieces. But it did come in, despite the fact that all the contributors could be told was that "something" was afoot to rescue the last Fenian political prisoners of the Rising of 1865. By late June the note to Richardson had been paid in full, the repair bills and the outfitting bills had been canceled and the gold was gathering for the expenses of the shore party.

When he opened his mail in the New York *Herald* office the morning after Independence Day, John Devoy read one letter with great interest. That night he hurried to John Breslin's modest flat a few steps off South Street on the lower East Side waterfront.

"I had a letter from John Talbot today," Devoy told him.

"Ah-ha!" Breslin pulled nervously at his long beard, and leaned forward in his chair. "Good news?"

"Good news indeed. They have over two thousand dollars collected in California. More important, they have chosen the man to go with you to Australia. They say they're ready any time we give the word."

"Who is he? Do I know him?"

"The name Talbot gives is Tom Desmond."

Breslin shook his head. "I don't recall anyone by that name, not that there aren't plenty of Desmonds in the old country. But I recollect no Tom."

"Nor I. But it doesn't matter, so long as Talbot vouches for him, as he does, without reservation. I'm sure Talbot has made a good choice. How soon can you start?"

Breslin's hearty laugh boomed in the room. "By the saints, John, am I never going to be able to stick to one job long in this country?" He scratched his head and figured for a moment. "The main thing is not to get anybody thinking the wrong things. Say I quit work the end of this week. Then I'll wander around the city a bit, and say I'm looking for a better job. Then I'll give out like I got a big chance on a railroad way out west and I got to hurry to Chicago to grab it. That ought to fool nosey ones."

"About two weeks?"

"Right."

"Then I'll write Talbot tonight and tell him he'll be seeing you soon so that he can tell Desmond. Now, Johnny, for the sake of all of us, and for the sake of our men, watch what you say!"

Breslin's hearty laugh boomed out again. "Didn't I hold my tongue when it came time to free Stephens in Dublin? There were some that couldn't stop their own cackling, you mind. Don't fear, no one will ever learn anything from Johnny Breslin!"

The night of July 18, 1875, Devoy visited Breslin again. Departure was set for the next morning. Breslin's belongings were packed in a single straw-matting suitcase and a bulging carpetbag.

"All ready, Johnny?" Devoy asked.

"All ready. I light out for my new job in the West tomorrow morning at ten. I've dreamed up a grand job for myself. Like as not I'll wind up president of the whole shebeen before I'm many years older." He grinned. "Now what more ought I know?"

Devoy pulled an envelope out of his waistcoat pocket. "This is a copy of the code I gave to Captain Anthony on the *Catalpa*," he explained. "There are secret messages here to take care of any situation. Guard it well, Johnny."

"I will!" Breslin tucked the envelope in his inner coat pocket.

"How long will it take you to get to the West Coast?"

"The ticket agent said if I make good connections in Chicago, and the train from there is on time, and we don't run into Indians or one of those big buffalo herds, about a week or ten days."

"Good. Now when you reach the Coast, get to Sacramento as quickly as you can. Go right to Talbot's house. He'll be waiting for you, for he must have my letter by now. He will get Desmond there to meet you."

"Does Desmond know I'm the leader of this expedition?"

"I've written Talbot that you are in sole charge of the land party and that your orders are to be obeyed without question by Desmond or anyone else, and that goes in this country and in Australia."

"You're sure Desmond understands that? I can't have any division of command."

"I told Talbot those are my orders. Desmond will obey."

"What about money? I don't have too much of my own."

"This isn't any job for you to spend your own money on, Johnny. The Clan will foot all the bills. If you ever have to use any of your own cash, keep account of it and the Clan will repay you." Devoy unbuttoned his coat and shirt and unfastened a money belt, which he handed to Breslin. "In this belt you'll find fifteen hundred in gold. And here—" he handed him another manila envelope—"is five hundred in greenbacks. Buy your ticket with the greenbacks and keep the gold on you at all times. When you get to Sacramento, Talbot will have more money for you and Desmond, and there'll be more in Australia. Any more questions?"

"What is Captain Anthony supposed to do when he gets there? He won't know me and I don't know him. How is he going to get in touch with me?"

"I've instructed the captain to make for Bunbury, which is

111

south of Fremantle, and register his ship with the proper port authorities there. All ship arrivals are posted on the telegraph bulletin board in Fremantle, O'Reilly says. All you'll have to do is watch out for the posting of the *Catalpa*. Then, and only then, will the code come into use. You'll find all the instructions written out for you."

"When do you want Desmond and me to leave for Australia?"

"That's up to you—and the steamer schedules. You ought to get there in time for their summer, say in October or November. That should give you good weather to get acquainted with the town, spy out the prison, find a good beach for the captain to use to take off our men. Desmond thinks you should stay at the Emerald Isle Hotel in Fremantle. The proprietor is Pat Maloney, a Fenian. But don't tell Maloney anything, Johnny. And don't even breathe your right name. If anyone hears 'John Breslin' . . ."

"I never forget the English have a price on my head," Breslin said. "And I know ten years isn't long in the memory of a vengeful Englishman—especially when it comes to remembering an Irishman."

"I know you will be careful, Johnny. This plan has to work. We'll never get another chance like it. If anyone even so much as thinks he recognizes you . . ."

"There's not much chance of that. I never had this before." Breslin tugged at his full beard. "When I was in Dublin I had a mustache, but now look at me, hiding behind this bush. Nobody will recognize the John Breslin of the Stephens jail delivery as . . . have you a name for me now?"

"I told Captain Anthony you would take the name of 'Collins,' that the man with you would be called 'Johnson.' Don't ever call yourselves by any other names."

"Collins . . . Johnson. Right."

"One thing more, the one man in Australia you can trust—that is, outside the walls of the prison—is Father Patrick McCabe. He helped O'Reilly. He has forwarded all the messages we have had from the men. He should be the key to unlock the door."

"He is the very first man I'll contact when I get to Fremantle!" Breslin promised.

Devoy put his arm around Breslin's shoulder. "I'm not going to run the risk of being seen with you when you leave tomorrow. So I'll say good-by to you now and wish you Godspeed. May the Holy Virgin guide you and protect you and bring you back safely—with our men."

He gave Breslin a final pat on the back and started back for his own lodgings.

At ten o'clock the morning of July 19, Breslin took ferry to Jersey City to board his train for the Far West. He made a good connection in Chicago and, despite all the dire warnings about unending buffalo herds that might block a train for hours, even a day, and about marauding Indians who would tear up rails, he arrived in San Francisco on July 26.

Next morning he secured accommodations on a river steamer for Sacramento and arrived there three days later.

Breslin found Talbot well situated in a new house on a quiet side street. A big man, and Irish to the core, he gave Breslin a grand welcome and insisted that while he was in Sacramento he must be his guest.

Talbot and Breslin walked around the town after the evening meal. Yes, he had had Devoy's letters. Where was Desmond? Only one man could put Breslin in touch with Tom. That was John Kenealy in Los Angeles. Desmond was on the go a lot. So a telegram should be dispatched to Kenealy. "Just wire Kenealy 'The fishing is good' and sign the name," Talbot said.

A whole week went by before two bearded strangers stepped down the gangplank of the river steamer from San Francisco and asked directions to the home of John Talbot. Distrusting the telegraph, Kenealy had come to Sacramento himself and had brought with him the man who was to be Breslin's companion in the shore party, Thomas Desmond.

Desmond was a tall, rawboned, bronzed man in his mid-thirties.

His quick blue eyes peered determinedly from beneath dark, beetling brows and a heavy shock of almost black hair.

"So you like fishing, Mr. Breslin," he boomed, as he pumped Breslin's hand. "We'll have a fine time trudging hither and yon looking for likely spots and maybe talking a bit on the side."

"Now talking about fishing is something I like almost as much as the catching of the fish." Breslin winked. He took an instant liking to this brawny Irishman.

Talbot provided rods and lines and creels, and for two weeks Breslin and Desmond tramped the woods and haunted the streams and visited backwoods camps and villages. Each night they came back with weighted creels.

But their catch was strange indeed. They netted not the blue backs of quivering trout, but the blue steel of a half dozen six-shooters; not the silver of a salmon's side but the nickel plate of two single-shot pistols. Their creels came back to Sacramento weighted with such things as ammunition, a half dozen caps, a half dozen pairs of pants. And, had anyone cared to look closely, he might have seen that on some of the nights when they returned to the Talbot home they seemed dressed uncomfortably for August, for under their fishing togs on at least three occasions each wore extra coats.

Clothes and arms for the Fenians thus secretly provided, Talbot urged they start for Australia at once. They left for Los Angeles on August 26. Kenealy put them up at his home where he had more money for them—$1,000 collected in small gifts and in large, from Irishmen who could ill afford to give more than a dime as well as from those who could afford an eagle or a double eagle in California gold. What greenbacks came in, Breslin converted them to gold and silver. Money belts weighed heavily around their middles.

"There will be more money for you when you get to Australia," Kenealy said. "We'll have an agent there who'll get in touch with you at the Emerald Isle Hotel. I'll see he knows who Collins and Johnson are. And it's time you started calling yourselves by those names to get used to them before you sail."

Desmond bowed low to Breslin. With a chuckle he said: "Mr. Collins, sir, thankee for your favors to a poor workman. Please to remember my name is Tom Johnson. I'll be most happy to serve you any time. May I know your first name, sir?"

Breslin shook his hand solemnly. "Mr. Johnson, I am happy to have made your acquaintance. The first name is John, sir, John Collins. Good-by now, Mr. Johnson. May we meet again on some most propitious occasion."

"My feelings entirely, Mr. Collins. And a good-by to you."

"But half a moment, Mr. Johnson. May I ask what your profession may be?" Breslin inquired most politely.

Desmond pondered for a moment. "In the States, my dear Mr. Collins, I have plied my trade as an honest carriage-maker," he said. "Why am I not, well, let us say, a slightly dishonest carriage-maker in Australia?"

"Capital!" Breslin nodded.

"And now, Mr. Collins, I do not think I have had the pleasure of knowing how you make a living."

"Why, did you not know, Mr. Johnson? I am a rich Yankee trader. I have pockets stuffed with gold and I'm seeking a chance to build a fortune in that grand land of opportunity, the fairest jewel in Her Gracious Majesty's Crown, the land of 'down under'—Australia." Breslin gave a courtier's bow. "And now, a true and fond farewell to one Thomas Desmond. God speed his journey and his voyage home."

Next morning they left for San Francisco and there engaged separate passages on the first steamer due to depart, the fast mail ship *Cyphranes*. As the wealthy Yankee trader, Breslin (as Collins) engaged the best of the first-class accommodations. Desmond (as the humble Johnson) grudgingly paid out his gold for second-class quarters and trudged aboard carrying his old-fashioned trunk on his shoulder. They saw little of each other on the voyage, as befitted passengers traveling in different worlds. At Sydney, they changed ship for Melbourne, then trans-shipped again to Albany, on King George Sound, and, finally, took the government steamer *Georgette* to Fremantle.

As the sun rose on the morning of November 16, Breslin and Desmond, now casual shipboard acquaintances, stood side by side and saw for the first time the "Golden Gate" of West Australia, Fremantle.

Desmond needed no words to tell him that the great glistening-white limestone pile that dominated the town was the prison. Breslin was interested in the activity going on at the dock, where, working at huge piles of lumber, were the inmates of that prison—all bearded and bronzed, all garbed alike, all healthy and strong, all seemingly young.

For all Breslin and Desmond knew, each and every one of the six men they had come so far to rescue might be working right before their eyes. Wilson, Darragh, Hogan, Harrington, Hassett, Cranston—they were names, nothing else, as far as their rescuers were concerned, for neither Breslin nor Desmond had ever laid eyes on any one of them. There were advantages in the fact that the rescuers could not know the prisoners, nor the prisoners the rescuers. A momentary flash of recognition, one startled word, one involuntary gesture and all would be lost.

Some of the convicts, under the direction of languid guards, grabbed hawsers and made the ship fast.

Desmond and Breslin walked down the gangplank—ashore at last in Australia. Desmond, in keeping with his humble station, trudged toward the center of the town, trunk on shoulder, asking directions to the stage for Perth, where Breslin had decided he should wait with the ammunition until the time for the rescue arrived.

Breslin, the wealthy Yankee, loudly called for a carriage, had his baggage put aboard, then, importantly, gave orders: "To the Emerald Isle Hotel, my man, and be smart about it!"

9 . A Yankee Trader Arrives in Australia

Desmond's stagecoach journey to Perth took him ten dusty miles.

Breslin's comfortable carriage took him but a few blocks over equally dusty but well-graveled town streets.

His driver pulled up with a flourish of whip before the door of a two-story frame structure across which was emblazoned in bright gold lettering: "Emerald Isle Hotel."

"I should like to engage your best room—your very best room, mind you. One that overlooks the *busy* street of this metropolis," Breslin said to Pat Maloney, the proprietor.

Breslin gave a critical look around the room to which he was shown. "If it is your best, I dare say it will do," he said. "Now I shall require fresh towels—those look a bit dusty—and some hot water . . ."

He grinned happily after the towels and the water had been delivered and he had turned the door key. Then he took two letters from his portmanteau and read them over for the first time since he had penned them back in New York.

New York, N. Y.
July 10, 1875

Mr. J. Collins, Esq.
Plains-on-Hudson, N. Y.

My dear Mr. Collins:
Please be advised that our syndicate directs me to inform you that, as of this date, one hundred thousand dollars has been deposited to your credit in the Hollanders Bank. You are to draw upon this sum as per our previous agreement. The other members of the syndicate are agreed that they will allow you to be sole

judge whether to invest the funds in Australian gold shares, timber, farm or grazing land.

My most humble respects.

Your obedient servant,
C. Coddington Yardley

That sounded almost good as gold. But the second letter—there was the clincher, he thought admiringly.

New York, N. Y.
July 12, 1875

Mr. J. Collins, Esq.
Plains-on-Hudson, N. Y.

Esteemed Sir,

Please be advised that the sum of one hundred thousand dollars has been placed to your credit in this bank. You may draw on it through our home office or by draft on any one of our numerous agents.

Most respectfully yours,
J. Carl. Hartman,
President,
Hollanders Bank of New York

Fondly Breslin gazed at his handiwork. That line of credit looked good enough to spend right now!

He left the letters on the small writing table, washed and went down to the lobby. Unless he misjudged human nature, the whole town of Fremantle would know, within twenty-four hours, that a wealthy Yankee trader was seeking opportunities for investment in Australia, in timber or mines or land.

He had lunch in the hotel dining room, left a silver dollar for the waitress, then took an exploratory stroll around the town. He walked along Market Street, turned on High Street, again turned on William, crossed Henderson, idled along the front wall of the prison, then took Perry Street to the Catholic church and back on Adelaide Street to High. The town seemed prosperous, with well-stocked shops and some fairly imposing buildings.

A Yankee Trader Arrives in Australia

He wandered down to the quay. A full-rigged ship, the *Horatio* of Liverpool, was being loaded with timber by a sweating gang of convicts. Breslin learned that no conversation was permitted with convicts. The slightest move on the part of a townsman even to pass the time of day with one of the brawny, bronzed men in prison garb brought an instant, sharp warning from one of the guards. He made mental note of that.

After an hour or more of watching the waterfront activities he wandered back to the hotel and up to his room. The letters were still atop the desk but their position had been changed. Someone— a chambermaid, perhaps—had read them. At supper time he could sense that they had done their job. The service had a touch of real deference. The waitress brought a few extra delicacies from the kitchen. The food was tasty and well cooked. He left a generous tip again and was bowed out by the help. The new guest, this polished man with the fine clothes, the imposing beard, the cultured voice, the well-filled purse, was a man of great importance indeed.

He repaired to the taproom for an after-dinner cigar and a brandy. A few rounds of drinks as a treat by the "Yankee" did no harm enhancing his status. So far, so good, he thought as he sipped his brandy. Now, the next step: a visit to Father Patrick McCabe.

It would, of course, be perfectly simple to call at the church rectory immediately. But that was the dangerous path. His meeting with the priest must be casual, it must have some sort of open and aboveboard reason, yet their conversation must be in secrecy. He'd have to put some real thought into the problem.

It was a hot, dusty walk the following Sunday from the hotel to the church. It was cool inside, however, cool and peaceful. The church, which might have held three hundred, was half-filled. Breslin walked to a forward pew and waited with interest his first glimpse of Father McCabe.

The congregation for this second and final Mass of the day was decently but not fashionably dressed. To Breslin they seemed honest villagers, small tradesmen, artisans, some probably from farms and hamlets nearby. Far in the rear sat a few aborigines—black fellows, as he had learned they were called. On the left side near the front, separated from the rest of the congregation, sat a small group of convicts in scrubbed prison garb, under the eyes of two guards.

The people hushed as the priest entered the sanctuary. Breslin studied him closely. He was in his mid-fifties, short, with a tendency to stoutness in his middle, and ruddy-cheeked from wind and sun. His features were kindly, his gray eyes had the crow's-feet of many smiles about them.

As he turned to the congregation, Father McCabe's eyes caught the face of a stranger. Gossip reached the priest as well as the villager. This full-bearded man with the fashionable clothes, the erect bearing, the intense gaze must be the "rich trader" just arrived from America.

His eyes caught, too, familiar faces in the convict group. Martin Hogan was one. Young Cranston was there too. At the earlier Mass others of the six he wanted so to help had taken Communion.

His thoughts raced back to a day about two weeks past, when Hogan had come to the rectory and stood, hat in hand, at the door, proffering a china dish, covered with a white napkin. "The Governor's compliments, Father," he said. "Here's a comb of fresh honey His Excellency says must do to pay in part for those grand eggs you sent him."

As the priest reachéd for the plate, Hogan had stepped close, looked furtively around, then, out of the corner of his mouth whispered: "Is there any word yet, Father?"

Sadly, Father McCabe had had to shake his head. "Patience, my son," he had said. "Patience. It is a long way to America. The mails travel slow."

"Patience, you say, Father!" Hogan frowned. "Patience! Have we not waited eight mean long years?" Hogan's voice grew even more bitter. "Indeed, eight centuries!"

"Yet still patience, my son. Eight years are but a tick in God's clock, a moment in the Eternity of man."

But Hogan replied: "Easy for you to say that, Father, you who are free to move and to breathe and to live. But eight years away from all you love—that is Eternity. There must be word soon. There must be a letter from America. You'll keep good watch, Father, won't you?"

What could he do but say as cheerfully as possible: "Of course I'll watch for the letter. Go into the church and pray to our Blessed Mother. She will hear your prayers."

The minutes with Hogan flashed through Father McCabe's memory in a few seconds. Despite his years of serving before his altar, the priest found himself standing motionless the while, looking out into the dim recesses of the church and especially at Hogan, kneeling there with the rest of the convicts. He turned abruptly to the altar and the Mass.

He blessed himself. Then: "Judge me, O God, and distinguish my cause from the nation that is not holy . . ."

The Mass progressed to its impressive close. Breslin felt a spiritual uplift. This simple bush pastor, in his quiet little church, touched him more than would a cardinal in his cathedral.

The following Sunday Breslin again took his seat far forward in the church and waited for Father McCabe to reach the point in the Mass, before the Confiteor, when he would make his simple parish announcements.

The priest had a bit of note paper in his hands as he raised his eyes to the congregation. Smiling slightly, he said: "I have here a communication that has touched me deeply. It is from one who has been a stranger in our congregation but who, from now on, must be reckoned as one to whom all our hearts will go out." His smile broadened and his eyes twinkled. "Mine especially. I refer, of course, to Mr. John Collins, the gentleman now seated before me."

He bowed in the direction of Breslin, who rose slightly and bowed in return. The congregation craned their necks to look. A buzz of whispers swept the church.

"Mr. Collins, as we all know, is from America and he is here on business.

"Now, I did not realize—" again the smile flitted over the

priest's ruddy face—"that my vestments were so threadbare it was noticeable to you people out there. I did know, of course, that our altar cloths were sadly worn. Now I am happy to say these particulars were quickly noted by the keen eyes of our visitor from the States, and he has most generously informed me that he wishes to present a set of new vestments and new altar cloths to the church. He has asked to see me in the sacristy after Mass this morning. Since I received the message just this very morning, I have had no opportunity to reply to him. But—" and he bowed again to Breslin—"if Mr. Collins will tarry awhile, I shall be most happy indeed to talk to him."

Breslin smiled pleasantly, but inwardly his spirits surged. None in the congregation or the town would suspect that today's conversation or any future ones with Father McCabe were anything but on matters connected with the parish.

It was some time before the last of the congregation had left off shaking Breslin's hand and departed. Finally he made his way to the sacristy door and knocked. Father McCabe took him by the hand and led him in.

"I don't know quite how to thank you, Mr. Collins," he said as he offered his visitor a chair.

"Thanks are not needed, Father. I am only too happy to do my little bit toward helping the church. But, first, Father, I have a confession to make."

The priest's eyes narrowed. "There is a time and a place for confession, my son."

"That I well know, but this confession is for your ears alone— your ears as a man, not as a man of God. I must tell you that my name is not Collins, Father."

"There are many in this land who use names other than their own, my son. That is no particular sin hereabouts."

"But I must reveal my real name and why I am here. First, let me tell you that we have a mutual friend, though he is a man you never saw. His name is John Devoy."

"John Devoy!" Father McCabe's eyes opened wide. "You know John Devoy of New York City?"

"Yes, and of Dublin too, Father."

Father McCabe excitedly got to his feet. "You are the one——" The priest halted his sentence in mid-air.

"I am, Father. I am John Breslin."

For a moment the priest looked puzzled. "Breslin? Breslin?" he repeated.

"Would it help if I reminded you of James Stephens?"

Father McCabe took both of Breslin's hands in his. "John Breslin, the man who freed James Stephens! I might have known Devoy would send the best here. I can't tell you how happy I am that you are here, Mr. Breslin. Our poor men have waited so long and so patiently. They've always believed their friends in America would help them."

"I hope I can help them, Father. But there is a tremendous amount of work to be done right here in Fremantle. I'm praying that you will help me."

"Of course I am ready to help you. We—and I speak for the six you have come after—know nothing of what is planned. In fact we have waited and waited for some assurance that there is some sort of plan afoot."

Breslin outlined all that had transpired in the States—and the fact that the *Catalpa* probably was at this very moment heading south from the Azores.

Father McCabe nodded approval as each step was unfolded. "Excellent! Excellent!" he said when Breslin had finished. "And now, what are you going to do before the ship arrives?"

"First I want to get in touch with one of the men as soon as possible. From what John Devoy has told me, Wilson should be the one. He is supposed to be a good organizer and a good planner. I would like to get a message to him, and then I want to meet him in secret somewhere, if that is possible and safe. I expect that right now it would be more prudent all around if we exchange messages through a trusted third party—meaning you, Father, if you will."

Father McCabe rubbed his chin reflectively. "I would be happy to help you in getting word to the men. But I don't have the daily contacts you need. The man we want to call in is Will Foley. He

123

was imprisoned here for his share in the Rising, but amnestied in
'71 along with most of the other political prisoners—except, of
course, our six. He is not a well man, his heart is ailing. But what
his heart may lack in physical strength, it more than makes up in
the way it beats for Ireland. He lives in Fremantle, does odd jobs,
runs errands. All the prison officers and guards know him. Not
one of them would suspect harmless Will Foley would be part of
a plot. Will Foley is the man."

"How do I get in touch with this Foley?"

"Leave that to me. I start on my weekly bush journey Tuesday
morning. Come to the rectory tomorrow night. I'll have Foley
there."

Will Foley, a wisp of an Irishman scarcely five feet tall, leaped
to his feet, bowing and scraping furiously, when the Yankee
trader entered the rectory parlor.

Breslin shook hands with the tiny man. "I've heard much about
you, Mr. Foley," he said. "I'd like to call you Will. Is that all
right?"

Foley turned to the priest, overwhelmed. "Do you hear that
now, Father? Mr. Collins would be friends with a poor soul like
meself! Ah, that such a day should come to Will Foley afore
he goes."

The priest laughed heartily.

"Come now, Will, it will be a long time before you join the
angels. Now, how about a bit of wine to hearten you?"

Foley's eyes brightened behind the spectacles. "Now would
you have a drop by you, Father?" he asked expectantly.

"Perhaps I have something a bit more equal to the task!" Breslin
interrupted. He pulled a flask from his pocket, poured a dram for
Foley, one for the priest and one for himself. Will put the glass
to his lips. His eyes widened. "Ah," he said. " 'Tis been so
long . . . You can taste the smoke in the malt!"

Foley drained his glass and rolled the last drop lovingly on his
tongue. Breslin filled the glass again.

"And now, Will, I want to ask you some questions."

"Anything, your honor."

"You know your way around the prison, do you not?"

Foley laughed mirthlessly. "I spent five years of my life there, didn't I?"

"Father McCabe tells me you have the run of the prison?"

"I do manage to get about in it, sir."

"Do you know a prisoner named James Wilson?"

Foley stared at him, thin lips tight shut.

"Do you?"

Foley looked at Father McCabe. The priest nodded.

"Maybe I do."

"Can you deliver a note to him so no one will know?"

Foley looked at the priest and again Father McCabe nodded. "That may be."

"Let me fill your glass. Will you drink to the glory of Ireland?"

Fire lit Foley's deep-sunk eyes. "That I will, and glad I am!"

"To the glory of old Ireland!" Breslin said solemnly.

They drained their glasses.

"Will, that note must be delivered to Jim Wilson for the sake of old Ireland. I have come from far off to get in touch with Wilson . . ." Breslin threw caution away. "And with Harrington, and Hogan, Hassett, Darragh and Cranston!"

Foley grabbed Breslin's hand. His eyes were wet. "Ah, now I know!" he said.

Father McCabe produced a bit of paper, a pen and ink. Breslin wrote: "To James Wilson and all the rest, greetings. Those who have not forgotten are close by. Take heart. The news from J.D. and J.B.O'R. is good. Trust the bearer. He will give you more news later. Destroy this for the sake of old Erin."

He did not sign it. He folded the bit of paper again and again to the size of a postage stamp. "Here, Will," he said. "Mind now, no one must see."

Foley stood erect as a soldier. He saluted. "And nary a soul but Jim Wilson will!"

10 . Contact

In the prison, the whitewashed walls threw back the morning sun's glare so brightly it almost blinded prisoners and guards alike at parade.

After breakfast—a pint of oatmeal and potato gruel, a chunk of bread and a half pint of unsweetened cocoa—the day's work parties were assigned. The six Irish political prisoners were trusties. Hogan drew his usual job of painter. Cranston reported to the storehouse. Darragh repaired to the lodgings of the Church of England chaplain where he daily acted as clerk and attendant. Hassett turned to in the superintendent's garden. Harrington was in solitary as punishment for trying to escape into the bush. Wilson, usually assigned to the docks with Harrington, got a surprise task—as an ex-cavalryman he was ordered to report to the stables, there to await the imminent arrival of the Comptroller General of West Australia and to see that his Excellency's horses were properly cared for and that the carriage was well washed and polished.

After looking around the docks in vain, Will Foley found Wilson in the stables. Two or three other prisoners were working nearby. Foley bided his time. In a moment when no one was looking he sidled up to Wilson and whispered: "Take what I give you. Don't look at it until you're alone." Into Wilson's hand he slipped the folded note from Breslin, then rambled away, whistling merrily.

Wilson grabbed a fork and began to spread bedding straw in one of the stalls being readied for the Comptroller's team. As he worked toward the rear of the stall he looked sharply about, saw

126

no one in sight and unfolded the bit of paper. His deep-set eyes raced over the words. Then he drank them all in again, this time ever so slowly. Softly he slapped his hand against his thigh. They had come! They had come! The prayers of eight years had been answered.

He read the note again, fixing every word in his memory. Then he put the bit of paper in his mouth, chewed it to a pulp and swallowed it.

As he worked mechanically, his mind was in a ferment. How were they going to stage the rescue? Would they dare the desert? It might be possible, given horses, supplies, maps. The sea? Small boats could never survive the voyage to a friendly port. A ship? What ship captain would chance offending the might of England? And who were "they"? Why hadn't the writer of the note signed it?

One thing was certain, the rest must know right away. Darragh would be the one to tell first. He had more freedom in moving around than any of them. He could spread the news.

He crowded next to Darragh in the mess hall that night. As they wolfed down their fare of a quarter pound of boiled beef, a half pound of soggy potatoes, a chunk of bread and a mug of tea, he whispered: "Red, listen sharp!"

Darragh went on eating as if he had heard not a word.

"I got a message today."

Darragh's eyes flicked over to his, then back stolidly to his pannikin.

Wilson looked cautiously around. "Will Foley brought it. It said 'Those who have not forgotten are close by . . .'" Darragh's jaws stopped working. Wilson looked around again. "J.D. and J.B.O'R. say take heart. Trust Foley. He'll bring more news later!"

Red mechanically swallowed another mouthful. "Thanks be to God, Jim! Who sent it?"

"I don't know."

"Didn't you ask Foley?"

"He was gone before I'd even read it."

"I'll lay for him tomorrow."

By the next morning, Red had spread the news to all but Harrington, still under guard in his dungeon cell.

Darragh met up with Foley shortly after noon that day. He put the question to Foley direct: "Who gave you that note, Will?"

"Father McCabe said it was all right," Foley said nervously.

"Of course it was all right. But who gave it you?"

"A big bearded man. Name of Collins. Says he's a rich man from America. Chaps here call him the 'Yankee.'"

There were visitors to the prison that very afternoon. If Red and Jim Wilson had known, they could have touched the very man who had written the mysterious message.

Bright and early that morning Maloney, the Emerald Isle proprietor, endeavoring to demonstrate his importance in the little world of Fremantle, asked his illustrious guest, Mr. Collins, if he would care to visit the chief attraction in the town, Her Majesty's prison. Mr. Collins would indeed be most happy to see the prison. Could Mr. Maloney arrange such a visit? Mr. Maloney could indeed. The superintendent, Mr. Donan, was a particular friend of his. He would send a message this very moment, stating that Mr. Collins, his noted guest, was desirous of seeing the Establishment. It would be no trouble at all, Mr. Collins could rest assured of that.

Thus, on the afternoon of Wednesday, December 2, the Yankee trader paid his respects to the man who headed the penal colony. Superintendent Donan insisted on conducting his guest around the grounds and the buildings in person.

"No doubt you are familiar with your great correctional institutions in the States, Mr. Collins," he said. "But you must realize that here we do not have the escape problems inherent in establishments built in more populous places. We depend here not on strong cells but upon our position betwixt sea and desert. The number of convicts who have made good an escape from this penal colony since it first was founded in the late 1700's could be counted on the fingers of one hand."

The *Catalpa*, from a Painting
by C. S. Raleigh, 1879

Captain George Smith Anthony

Samuel P. Smith, First Mate
of the *Catalpa*

John Boyle O'Reilly

John
Devoy

John J.
Breslin

The Prison at Fremantle

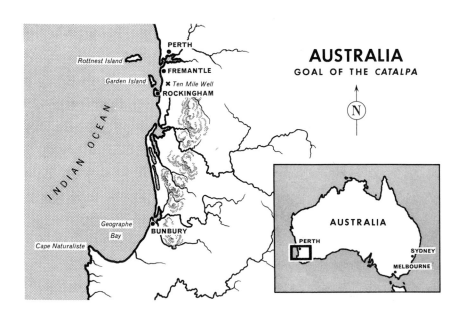

His visitor nodded appreciation.

"We have but one prisoner in our punishment cells at the moment," Superintendent Donan boasted as he showed Breslin the dungeon block. "That speaks rather well for the discipline of the prisoners as a body, does it not?"

"It does indeed," his guest agreed. "This man wouldn't be a Yankee, would he?"

Donan laughed. "No, Mr. Collins, he's not a compatriot of yours, though I believe we have one or two who may be Americans—if they'd confess it. He's an Irish traitor. We have a number of them here. And, I must tell you, they are all real troublemakers."

They paused before a bolted door.

"This is the occupied cell," the superintendent said.

From within came a muffled, "Get the hell away! Let me alone."

"He will be alone for quite a few weeks yet," Donan commented.

The familiar iron door, the all too familiar iron bolts, the two-inch crack at the bottom to admit air—it was all much like the prison Breslin had served in in Dublin. If he could only speak for just one moment to that Irishman to assure him friends were here, that escape was indeed possible!

Breslin turned away, sick at heart, yet more determined than ever that he would succeed.

Foley carried another message to Wilson: "We have reconnoitered the prison. We have a definite plan for your rescue. How long will Harrington be in solitary?" This time Foley waited until Wilson had a chance to read and destroy the message.

"Do you know any more about this man?" Wilson demanded of the little Irishman.

"I do not, Jim, so help me."

Wilson thought awhile. "Tell him Harrington will be out about the middle of January. Got it?"

In a few days there was another note. "Success depends on all of you men being trusties. You must be model prisoners at all times."

This time Wilson scribbled a reply on the back of the note. "Will it help if we know who you are? Can you identify yourself?"

When Breslin read this he decided he should have another talk with Father McCabe. At the rectory, he put the problem squarely before the priest.

"Father, these men have a right to know more about our plan. And they have a right to know who is over here to help them. There are too many things to settle on bits of paper. I must meet Wilson. You're the only one who can help me. Foley can't do more than he has done, that's sure."

A broad smile creased the priest's ruddy face. "I've been waiting for you to say that. I haven't been idle, you know. In fact, I've been doing a little planning of my own for just this occasion ever since you first told me why you were in Australia. To tell the truth, I've been a bit of a puzzle to some of the natives hereabouts who thought they knew me through and through. Especially the boys down at Albert's Livery. You see, I've most always hired a horse or a donkey for my trips out back. But lately, strangely enough, I've hired a trap. Now I really think they figure I'm getting along in years and I can't take the saddle any more. Be that as it may, with a trap . . ."

"You can carry a passenger!"

"You catch on very quickly for a Yankee," Father McCabe jibed. "Yes, I can take a passenger. I seem to recall that one of my parishioners has had some great trouble with one of his horses lately. Wilson, you know, is pretty good with animals. I can't think of any man who can help me out in this task other than Jim Wilson, can you?"

"If by some miracle you can get him out of prison duties and into the carriage," Breslin said, a trifle cynically.

"Now you just leave that to me. I haven't been in and out of the prison here for a quarter of a century for nothing. Superintendent Donan, pompous as he is, always has been most helpful when I have asked his aid in the past. I'm sure he will lend me Jim for the day."

"You'll get Wilson out on the road somewhere and I'll meet up with you . . ."

"Whoa, now, hold your horses." Father McCabe held up a warning hand. "Let's get some details straight before we go off half cocked. Here is my plan, listen closely. Do you know the road that leads from Fremantle to Ten Mile Well and Rockingham?"

"I think so."

"Be sure you know. Hire a rig and drive out the road. About four miles out of town, on your left, you will see a huge lightning-blasted gum tree. You can't miss it. Fix that spot in your mind. Now, whenever I get Wilson for my helper, I'll send you a note. I'll say, 'That timber deal is shaping up,' and add a time element, like 'morning is the best time,' and I'll add the hour I expect to be at the gum tree."

"And I'll drive out and meet you there."

"I'm surprised at you." Father McCabe shook a finger. "The liberator of Stephens should know better than that! I'll drive past the tree and drop Wilson off. He'll go back into the bush a piece. I'll pull ahead a few yards until I see you drive up. Then I'll jog slowly for a mile or so. Now when you get to the tree, get out of your rig and start back into the bush as if you were going to make water. Wilson will be watching for you. I'll give you twenty minutes. Then I'll be back and pick Jim up."

"Twenty minutes isn't much," Breslin said slowly. "But if that is all you think we should risk, it will have to do. Now to get Wilson out."

"I'm not going to be in any hurry," Father McCabe warned.

Father McCabe was not in any hurry. It was not until the new year of 1876 had come in that the priest made his move.

Fretting and fuming inwardly the while, Breslin put in his time making carriage trips to various towns in the neighborhood of Fremantle. One of his first jaunts was out Ten Mile Well road. He spotted the gum tree rendezvous easily. On another occasion he visited Perth and, on pretext of having a bolt repaired on his carriage, visited Sloan's Carriage Factory, where Desmond had written he was employed, and managed to tell him of the progress he had made and of the imminent meeting with Wilson.

At Christmas the "rich Yankee trader," who so far had paid little heed to the glowing proposals made him by natives, found himself invited to a reception for His Excellency, Governor Robinson. Hobnobbing with the genial state officials he hoped soon to hoax gave Breslin a secret laugh.

Father McCabe sent his code note before breakfast Monday, January 3. It fixed the hour of nine for the meeting. Breslin hurried to Albert's Livery Stable and hired a good horse and buggy. Within minutes of the hour he reached the gum tree. Ahead he saw Father McCabe's trap. The priest waved to him, tapped his nag, and vanished in a dusty cloud down the road.

Breslin tethered his horse to a tree. The road as far as he could see in either direction was deserted. On its sides the forest closed in like a green wall. The cries of thousands of cockatoos and the strident buzz of millions of insects filled the air.

Breslin took a couple of steps off the road into the brush. A twig snapped under his foot. Instantly the birds hushed into suspicious silence.

From the bush to the right of the gum tree came a low whistle.

Breslin took one more look up and down the deserted road.

He entered the bush, pushing branches aside as he made his way.

"This way!" came a hoarse whisper.

Breslin took a few more steps and came to a tiny clearing, where stood a man in prison dress. He held his prison hat in his hand. A shock of brown hair, parted roughly on the right side, tumbled over a broad, high forehead and shadowed deep-set gray eyes. A beard covered the lower half of his long, thinnish face. He took a step forward and held out his hand. "I'm Jim Wilson," he said.

Breslin grabbed his hand. "I've been looking forward to this moment for months, Jim."

Relieved, happy though he was, Wilson could not keep the bitterness out of his voice. "Months!" he said. "We've been waiting for eight years . . ."

Breslin held up a warning hand. "We haven't much time. Father McCabe said he would give us twenty minutes. Has he told you anything?"

"Only who you are. I am proud to shake the hand of the man who freed James Stephens."

"Then we have a lot to cover in a few minutes. I am not alone over here. We have another man in Australia, Tom Desmond from America. You don't know him. We are here to carry out the plan that John Devoy and John Boyle O'Reilly and your friends in the States think is the only one that has any chance of success."

"We had a plan of our own," Wilson countered. "It would have worked too, had we some guns."

"Our plan is to get you off like John Boyle O'Reilly got away," Breslin said.

Wilson had an instant objection. "How are you going to bribe a sea captain to take a half dozen of us aboard? It took a hell of a lot of hard work on the part of the Father to get O'Reilly alone away. You'll never do it with a gang of us!"

"There'll be no need to bribe a passing sea captain. We have the ship!" Breslin paused to let the fact sink in.

"You have the ship?" Wilson asked, bewildered. "I don't rightly understand."

"I mean just that. The Clan has bought an American whaleship just to rescue you men."

"Bought a whole ship?" Wilson still could not believe his ears.

"Yes, we bought it. We haven't been idle. Irish patriots all over the world have almost thirty thousand dollars invested in this plan."

Wilson shook his head in utter disbelief. "A ship! Thirty thousand dollars! For us!"

Breslin went on. "The ship is under command of a Yankee skipper. She started out from New Bedford, in Massachusetts, long before John Devoy sent me out to California to join up with Desmond. She is due to arrive in Bunbury in late February. When she gets here, the captain will get in touch with me. I'll contact you men, you'll escape from the prison, the captain will land a whaleboat on a beach somewhere near here and he'll pick you up, row you out to his ship and set sail for New York. How does that sound?"

"Too good to be true." Wilson still shook his head. "You make it sound simple, but it ain't goin' to be that simple."

"We think it will work. The main thing is for all you men to be on your good behavior and to be working outside the prison walls when the time comes. That's something you'll have to figure out for yourselves. You'll all have to be trusties."

"They call 'em 'constables' here," Wilson put in.

"Constables, then. You'll have to be as free to walk through the gate as it is possible to be. Can you do it?"

"If you could say be ready in the next couple weeks, I'd say it *was* easy. They're going to build a new reservoir at the prison this month. All of the outback road and timber gangs have been called in. All the work details will be on the reservoir and on the docks where the materials will come in. But after that . . ."

"We'll have to hope for the best. Main thing is to make the men realize rescue depends on all of them getting to the constable grade. Tell them about the plan. Tell them I'll keep in touch with them by notes through Foley to you. Tell them to trust us to get them away. I'll figure out a code so you and I can communicate if need be."

From the road came a low: "Cooee!"

"That will be the Father," Breslin said. "You'd better go now. Trust us, keep your mouths shut, wait till you hear more from me."

They shook hands. Wilson pushed his way out to the road and climbed into Father McCabe's trap. The priest whipped his horse to a smart trot in the direction of Ten Mile Well. A few minutes later Breslin untied his horse and drove slowly back to Fremantle.

At the Emerald Isle, Breslin was buttonholed by yet another one of the countless businessmen and bankers, miners and land-owners who had been trying for weeks to get their hands on some of his Yankee gold. He had listened to practically every get-rich-quick scheme that could be dreamed up by willing—and wily—natives. Gossip was increasing because he never seemed inter-ested in plans to double, triple or quadruple his investment. There were rumors that he had no money at all, that he was only an adventurer.

Truth to tell, the money belt that had been so heavy around his middle when he had arrived in Fremantle was getting lighter and lighter—much lighter than was safe. Living like a rich man had taken its toll of the eagles and double eagles. The latest drain had been to Will Foley. Foley, convinced at last that his heart would fail him soon, had confided in Father McCabe that he hoped to live to see the old country once again. It seemed little enough, Breslin thought, for all Foley was doing for him, to advance pas-sage money and enough for him to have a few weeks back in Erin. All he asked of Foley was that he postpone the voyage home until he no longer was needed as a go-between.

That Sunday night at the rectory, Breslin broached the most important step still facing him: the choice of a landing place for Captain Anthony's whaleboat.

"You know the whole region, Father," he said. "I'm going to ask you to pick the spot."

"I have given that much thought, too," the priest said. "In fact, I've already done a little bit of looking."

"O'Reilly got off in a boat. How about the spot where he was rescued?"

"Bunbury? Too far. You want a beach near enough to Fre-mantle so you can get to it with your horses at a trot or a gallop. You don't want to be so far away that your teams will fag out and the police catch up with you. They'll travel a lot faster on horse-back than you will in wagons. I have a spot in mind. Come with

me on my bush trip this week. You can give out that you are going to look at some timberland around Rockingham. There's a
lumbering outfit working thereabouts."

Tuesday morning Breslin hired a pair of Albert's best horses
hitched to a light buckboard, then picked up the priest at the
rectory.

"Head out the same road where you met Wilson," Father Mc-
Cabe directed. "After we pass Ten Mile Well and Rockingham
Hotel, it's about four miles farther."

The first ten miles to the Well was over a macadamized, convict-
built road. From Ten Mile Well to Rockingham Hotel were six
miles of heavier going, with deep sand patches that slowed the
horses to a walk.

Finally they turned off the road onto a track wide enough for
logging teams. The going was slow, with the sand deep. The air
was close and heavy as dense forest closed in on either side,
scraping the sides of the rig. Then the bush thinned and they
drove out on beach sand, fairly hard packed.

Breslin and the priest breathed in the fresh ocean air appreciatively. A light surf sighed and whispered along a stretch of
pure white sand. Offshore, perhaps a hundred yards, the blue of
deep water showed. Breslin nodded. "It's right," he said. "Right
as rain."

They sat down for an hour until the horses were well rested,
then started the team on the home journey. Winding up with a
smart gallop on the hard road from Ten Mile Well to the out-
skirts of Fremantle, they found that the horses had covered the
entire twenty miles in two hours and twenty minutes.

"With a fresh team I can clip ten minutes from that," Breslin
boasted.

January dragged into February.

Breslin haunted the ship bulletin board.

There was no word from Captain Anthony.

There was no word either from the men Kenealy had promised
would deliver more gold for the expedition. He counted the gold
he had left, and concluded he could remain the "rich Yankee

trader" for just about one month more—until about the first week in March.

Foley brought a note from Wilson: "Harrington's got out of solitary but they put him on a timber gang. They said there wasn't going to be any more details until the reservoir is done, but they cooked one up to punish Harrington some more and some others that they wanted to punish. No word when he will get back. He don't know about the plan. He's like to try to run away. If he does he'll get solitary again. Nothing we can do now."

Again Breslin heard gossip about himself. To put a stop to the rumors he used some of his dwindling store of cash to hire a team, announcing he was going on a business trip. He drove to Guilford, York, Northam, Newcastle and Perth. In Perth he managed a few minutes with Desmond, still working steadily for Sloan.

"The ship has to show up soon," he told Tom. "When she gets in and I've talked to the captain, I can send you a telegram about starting. Have a good team ready to be hired at all times. And when you start, don't forget the clothes and the guns and cartridges."

On March 5 three burly strangers arrived. One bragged he was from New South Wales and was heading for the goldfields of the northwest. He demanded the names of the hotels in Fremantle and settled for the Emerald Isle. His two traveling companions wandered off in search, they said, of any cheap but clean lodgings, any honest work and "To hell with the goldfields." The stranger signed the Emerald Isle's register, "George Jones, Sydney, N.S.W."

"I understand you have a guest here by the name of Collins," he addressed the clerk. "I have a very personal letter from one of his banking connections in Sydney."

The clerk took him to Breslin's room and introduced him. The stranger closed the door behind him and slid home the bolt.

Breslin raised his eyebrows. "What was that for?"

"I want secrets kept too," the stranger countered. "John King, at your service. I think I have what you have been waiting for." He reached under his shirt and undid a money belt, and slapped it down on the table. "There's eight hundred pounds sterling,"

137

he said. "And I dare say I can put my hands on a few pounds more if need be."

The funds, he explained, had been collected from Irish sympathizers in New Zealand and in New South Wales.

He had been in touch by mail with Kenealy who had written him some of the plans for the break. "You did not see my friends," he said. "There are two more in my party, Denis F. McCarthy of Cork, and John Walsh, lately of Dunham, England. All three of us were in the Organization and all of us were amnestied in '71. What can we do to help?"

"Two men will be needed to cut the telegraph wires between Fremantle and Perth and between Fremantle and Rockingham and Bunbury. I'll need a man to ride rearguard when we head for our rendezvous."

"I'm your man for the rearguard," King said. "McCarthy and Walsh will cut the wires."

"It's lucky you arrived this day," Breslin said as they talked on. "Tomorrow I'm for Bunbury to see if I can get word of our ship."

11 . "No News from New Bedford"

In the days of sail, the whaler was a lonely craft. It was a ship going nowhere, a ship that cruised endlessly and erratically on the face of the deep. It had no port of call beckoning at the end of weary miles. It had no freight to transport, no passengers to take from one country to another. Its whole reason for existence was to find a spot anywhere in the seven seas where a school of sperm spouted.

This is what the crew of a whaler expected. That is what the crew of the *Catalpa* was ready to take as a matter of course.

But the forecastle oracles were quick to note, now, that the *Catalpa* was a whaler with a purpose. And that purpose certainly was not the hunting of whales. Instead of the slow, monotonous search of empty seas for her prey, she held to a steady tack that took her well off the coast of Africa, past Ascension Island, rocky outpost of England's might, on and on toward Capetown. Not that the crew could see the log or the well-marked charts. Not that any of them save Smith, Farnham and Bolles, now back aft again as Third Mate, could have taken a navigational sight to fix their position in the vastness. But to all of them came the realization that the *Catalpa* was not acting like other whalers on which they had sailed. Lookouts were always kept in the masthead rings, but they raised no spouts. Three weeks went by and the *Catalpa* forged steadily on. Forecastle mutterings grew.

Then, on December 19, the cry "Ah . . . *blooows!*" rang from aloft.

Luck was with the crews. Three small whales fell to the darts and lances. But they boiled only forty barrels all told.

139

Now the forecastle seethed. Months at sea and not enough oil shipped or in the hold to buy a night's fun in a grogshop. Hill found ready ears for his tirades.

"Who in hell ever heard o' such like whalin'?" he demanded. "We ain't huntin' whales. We're a goddam ghost ship. We're sailin' hell bent for nowhere. Why'n hell don't our goddam Captain get to the Plate? I bin down thar. Sparm thicker'n bones in a herrin'. Who's with me to ask the Captain what the hell's he doin' wastin' time?"

The deputation hadn't got as far as the tryworks before Captain Anthony shouted the men to a halt.

"Now what's this? What devilment are you up to now, Hill? Haven't you had enough of irons to last you the rest of your life? Speak up if you got a gripe. I'll mighty soon settle your hash!"

"We want whales. We want more oil in the hold!" Hill said.

"Oil, is it? Don't you think I want oil in the ship's casks same's you?"

"Then let's head for the Plate like we cleared for. Them's good whalin' grounds."

"We'll head wherever I please. This is my ship. I'm earning money for her owners. No seaswab aboard this bark gives me orders. One more squeak out of you on this voyage and I swear I'll chase sharks and the bait on the hook will be a troublemaker named Hill. Now get forward, the passel of you!"

The *Catalpa* rolled uneasily along. At last there were favoring winds, though they were light. The bark's fouled bottom held her back in such airs, and there was neither the time nor the place to careen to scrape off the seaweed and the barnacles.

Late in the afternoon of the day before Christmas, First Mate Smith's boat darted and lanced a small whale. The tryworks flamed all night. It was a hot, dirty, greasy, surly crew that tapped the last of only twenty barrels of oil from the cooling tanks into the casks.

That sultry holy night, under blue stars that flickered through the pall of oily smoke, the bark crossed the Equator.

On Christmas Day the cook concocted a pudding from flour,

water, molasses, whale oil, soda, spices and some of the dates that had been shipped in the Canaries. He fried up some whale tongue. The Captain doled out an orange apiece from the few remaining in the crates and broke out a small cask of wine from the vineyards of Teneriffe. Some of the men pounded hardbread into powder, and mixed it with molasses to make samp.

For two months the bark bore monotonously onward. Never was there more than a hatful of wind. No more sperm were sighted, though a few finback whales were raised. Once or twice the boats were lowered and gave chase, but the finbacks gallied and none was darted.

In his cabin, with Sam Smith leaning over his shoulder, Captain Anthony worked with charts, protractors and dividers. There was no getting around it, the bark could never make Bunbury in February. It would be almost a miracle if she got there much before the end of March.

Four thousand miles from Teneriffe to Capetown. Four thousand, seven hundred miles from Capetown to Cape Naturaliste, off the West Australian coast south of Bunbury. There were no short cuts. The charts were there, infallible. Mile after mile after mile must be sailed. Promises had been made to John Devoy but the facts were indisputable. Bunbury by the end of March— if then.

Captain Anthony put his protractor down with a shake of his head. "We aren't going to make Bunbury any time near what I promised. We'll be lucky if we get there by the first of April at the rate we're going."

"Mebbe we'll get some decent wind."

"Maybe. Something we can't bet on—can only pray for, I guess. I'm worried that Breslin will be figuring on the end of February, as Devoy planned, and will have all his men ready then. Then we don't show up and everything's ruined."

It couldn't be helped. They were somewhere off the southern tip of Africa—well at sea, away from Capetown and prying English eyes. If there were winds, perhaps they could make up a few lost days in the long slant across the Indian Ocean. Just perhaps.

The winds came. Thursday night, February 10, the sun went down in a dirty sky. The *Catalpa* was bowling along under every stitch of canvas Captain Anthony could hang on her yards. "Keep pushing her!" he ordered Bolles when the Third Mate came on night watch at eight in the evening.

Bolles kept pushing her. At ten o'clock a heavy breeze blew up from the south-southwest. The bark dug her bow deep into mounting waves, hurling stinging spray over the rails. Bolles eyed the straining sails but kept the canvas drawing full.

By the middle of the morning watch, a tremendous cross-sea built up. A full gale roared through the rigging, threatening to carry away the few rags of canvas still spread. Solid seamanship demanded that even these sails be taken in. But in the back of Captain Anthony's mind was the warning of the *Catalpa's* officer back in East Boston: "Take in your topsails and she'll roll over!"

Great white-maned combers racing at each other from opposite quarters in the maelstrom of wind and sea, slammed into each other with a noise like thunderclaps and flung up mountainous cascades of spray. In such a cross sea there wasn't a man aboard who could not see the danger of being swamped. Neither ship nor canvas could longer take such punishment.

"We'll heave to, Mr. Smith," Anthony ordered.

Slowly the bark swung into the teeth of the gale. A more violent gust struck her. The ship balked and trembled. The lower fore topsail split at the weather clew and ripped to shreds.

"Look alive, Mr. Smith!" Anthony yelled. "We're in for it, or those chaps in Boston don't know what they're talking about."

By all the rules of wind and waves, a flat-bottomed craft like the *Catalpa* had to have some sails showing so that she would not roll to windward and be swamped.

The bark shook and plunged, then reared back like a frightened horse, and came up into the wind gracefully and buoyantly to sit the waves like a duck.

Captain Anthony wiped the sweat from his forehead. That was one time when the prophets of doom were dead wrong.

By noontime the wind had abated somewhat and the bark was put on her course again, with more sails spread and the wind-shredded topsail replaced with one of the new ones bought at Fayal. At midnight the gale blew itself out. The wind dropped to a stiff breeze. Again all the *Catalpa's* big sails were set and at daybreak she was bowling smartly along.

For eleven days, from February 29 to March 10, the wind blew strong from nearly dead ahead. The *Catalpa* lay to most of the time under lower topsails and staysail. Rain squalls swept over them constantly. When the skies finally cleared enough so that Captain Anthony could take a fix on his position, he discovered the bark had made only 120 miles in all that time, a month late and still making so little headway.

But at last the ship's luck changed. The winds served strong and fair. She coursed along like a race horse, as if knowing she was on the homestretch of her voyage. Under full sail, she logged more than two hundred miles some days. Late in the afternoon of March 27, the masthead lookout yelled, "Land ho! Dead ahead."

Blue-gray in the distance loomed what the Captain knew was Cape Naturaliste. To the men it might be New Zealand, or it might be Mozambique, or Africa, or the coast of South America. All they cared was that land meant a port where the ship would refit and revictual. A port meant a place where there was rum and women. They could buy gear in the ship's slopchest, take it ashore and trade for the rum and women. What did the country matter? Rum was good, women were the same the world over.

To George Anthony, the blurred mass arching around the southern and eastern horizon meant an end to a year of hard work, of frustration, and of worry. The *Catalpa* was at her rendezvous with Fate—and weeks late for the meeting. What the delay would mean to Breslin and his shore party and the six desperate men who waited for rescue, only the next few days could tell.

The *Catalpa* skirted the shoreland, Cape Naturaliste well to starboard. In the gathering dusk the lights of Dunsborough twinkled. Anthony set a northeasterly course through Geographe Bay, heading for Leschenault Inlet near the harbor of Bunbury. Fearing to hazard the shoal waters of the bay in darkness, he ordered sails furled and a single bow anchor dropped.

At five o'clock in the morning, the anchor was hoisted, and the *Catalpa* got under way again, under light sails. At ten in the morning she was safely in the harbor of Bunbury.

"Both anchors, Mr. Smith!" the skipper ordered.

Anchors holding, sails furled, the Captain ordered his whaleboat overside.

Second Mate Farnham was left in charge. "No shore leave until I register, Mr. Farnham," the Captain ordered as he and First Officer Smith slid down the davit falls into the boat for the trip ashore.

Captain Anthony went at once to the customs office.

"Captain George Anthony, reporting the arrival of the bark *Catalpa,* out of New Bedford, United States of America, whaling."

"Glad to have you in Bunbury, Captain," the customs official replied. "Your papers?"

Anthony handed them over. The official scanned them rapidly.

"Captain, your papers seem in order. We require that you give us notice when you sail."

"That you shall have, sir."

Captain Anthony bundled up his papers and left to look for Sam. He found him gazing longingly into a shopwindow full of glittering golden ornaments, his mind on a gift for his Amy Chase.

"Time enough for that later, Sam. Let's get back to the bark."

They had not been rowed more than a dozen yards from shore when Sam pointed excitedly. "Look, Cap'n, her flag's upside down!"

"Lay on them oars!" Anthony thundered. "What the devil's wrong now?"

When they boarded the *Catalpa,* Farnham was screaming mad. His words came in a sputtering torrent.

"That goddam Hill. He's no good fer nothin'. One minute I go

144

below. One minute. That goddam Hill and that Coeking an' that Duguin an' that Paine, they put boat overside. I come on deck. I yell, 'Stop, you t'ieves.' They say, 'You goddam Brava you go t' hell!' I run to side. I try to put belayin' pin in boat falls. That goddam Hill knock belayin' pin outa my han's. Those t'ieves drop boat in water. They grab oars. They row lak hell. That goddam Hill t'umb nose at me. Me who am mate! I catch him I giv' him hell like he never got afore. I skin blubber off him wid cuttin' spade. No cap'n ever hire him fer sailor agin. I tell every cap'n in whole dam worl' no ship goddam Hill!"

Farnham had lowered another boat, but Hill and his three companions reached the beach far ahead of him and scrambled ashore. Farnham had the deserters' boat brought back to the bark.

"Well, Sam, looks like we better row back ashore," Anthony said in disgust. "We'll report them to the Water Police."

Halfway to shore, a Water Police cutter slipped alongside. The coxswain in charge yelled: "Those your men got away, Cap'n?"

Anthony nodded.

"We'll round 'em up. They won't get far."

The Captain and Sam continued their journey ashore and went to the Water Police barracks to wait. The police were as good as their word. In three hours they had the four deserters under arrest.

"Any charges, Captain?" the Water Police coxswain asked.

"No, no charges," he replied. "Just run them down to my boat for me."

"All right, you men, march!" the coxswain ordered.

Coeking flew at him. "I'm sick of whalin'. You can't make me go back." He hauled off and caught the policeman a glancing blow on the shoulder.

"Strike an officer, will you? Now I have some charges to prefer! Lock him up!" the Water Police officer shouted.

Hill, Duguin and Paine went back to the ship meekly enough, where they were put in irons in the steerage.

"I'm going ashore again, Sam," Captain Anthony told the First

Mate. "If Breslin does what he's supposed to do, he'll read news of our arrival on the telegraph bulletin board in Fremantle. He'll be trying to get in touch with me. If you need me, I'll be at the hotel—there only seems to be one decent-looking one."

He reached the town's best hotel—Spencer's—registered and went to his room. It had been a busy day, and a bad day. A bad way indeed to start the affair in Australia with the attention of the local police drawn to the *Catalpa* from the moment she had dropped anchor. But it could have been worse. Desertions were an old story to the police. Many a whaler had the same experience when the anchors were dropped and the smell of the land reached the nostrils of sea-weary sailors. There was no use worrying.

Restless and awake by daybreak on March 29, Breslin stepped out for his morning walk just as the sun was peeping up.

Hands deep in pockets, head bent, he walked listlessly toward the telegraph office. Again he wearily pondered the possibilities if the *Catalpa* had indeed been lost. There still remained almost $3,000 of the gold King, Walsh and McCarthy had brought from New South Wales. That wasn't enough to tempt any Yankee skipper to try and smuggle out six convicts—at the risk of his own liberty. One, maybe, as in the case of O'Reilly, but six! Not a chance. No matter how much he debated, it looked as if failure was near. The Fenians would rot in jail the rest of their lives. There would be no more news this day than in the days past.

As he approached the telegraph office he spotted several new notices tacked on the board. Instinctively he quickened his steps. But with accustomed disappointment he read: "Arrived at Sydney, British ship *Borneo* . . . Arrived, Adelaide, mail packet *Gloria* . . ."

Then, just below, almost hidden in the litter of bulletins, another:

> "Arrived at Bunbury, American whaling
> bark *Catalpa*, out of New Bedford,
> Capt. Anthony, March 28."

Breslin slapped his thigh and laughed aloud. They made it! He looked sharply the length and the width of the street, but there were no other early-risers in sight to see his joy.

He dashed back to the Emerald Isle, hurried to his room, bolted the door. From the bottom of his bag where it had lain all these long months, he took Devoy's code. Nervously he thumbed the pages. Here it was! Fingers trembling with excitement, he copied the code message that would be his first communication with Captain Anthony.

The telegraph office would not open until nine. He tried to calm himself and went down to breakfast at his usual time, striving to look unruffled. Even though he stretched the meal longer than usual he was finished long before the hour. Nevertheless, he took off for the telegraph office and there paced the sidewalk until the operator arrived for business.

"I have an urgent message for one of my captains who has just arrived in Bunbury," Breslin said importantly. "I would appreciate it greatly if you would transmit it immediately." He pushed his message across the window, a silver piece weighing the paper down. "For you," he murmured.

"Thank you, sir! I shall send the message at once."

The message read: "To Capt. Anthony, Master, Bark *Catalpa*, Bunbury. Have you any news from New Bedford? When can you come to Fremantle? J. Collins."

Captain Anthony arose that March morning after his first night's sleep in a real bed since he had left the warm arms of Emmie. He felt like a new man. After breakfast at Spencer's, he decided to arrange for supplies, fresh meat and other provisions, and then visit the local telegraph office to arrange for the delivery of any messages for him.

From a ship's chandler, Captain Anthony trudged to the telegraph office. The operator in charge was a taffy-haired, pink-and-white-complexioned English girl.

"My name is George Anthony. I'm master of the *Catalpa*, anchored in your harbor. I am expecting a——"

Just then the telegraph sounder clicked.

"Pardon me, sir." The girl stepped to the instrument. "I'll be but a moment."

Within two minutes she came back to the window. "Well, isn't that the strangest thing ever!" she said. "That message was for you!"

She handed him Breslin's telegram neatly copied in a copperplate hand on the regulation form. "Will there be any reply, sir?"

"Thank you, miss, yes, I'll be back shortly with a message for Mr. Collins."

In his room, he dug the Devoy code from his bag. Thumbing through its pages he came on the proper message: "No news from New Bedford. Shall not come to Fremantle." According to the penciled note against the wording, this would tell Breslin that there had been no suspicious incidents on the voyage, that all was well, and that Breslin should come to Bunbury as soon as possible.

He walked back to the telegraph office, where he fretted a half hour while the girl transmitted messages and received others. Finally she gave the sending key a final rattle and came to the window.

"Now, Captain, what can I do for you?" She brushed back an errant blond curl with ink-smudged fingers.

"I have a message for Fremantle."

"Is it government business?"

"No, but it's urgent."

"I'll send it directly I have lunch."

"I tell you, it's urgent. It's to one of my owners!" Anthony sputtered.

The girl's pink cheeks flushed. With tapping fingers she emphasized her words. "Sorry, but I'm fair done in. First thing after lunch." She slammed the window shut.

In Fremantle, Breslin fretted and fumed the whole day. What on earth kept Anthony from replying? Flinging all caution away, he asked the telegraph operator time after time if there had been any answer to his message to "his captain" at Bunbury. With more and more scowling a countenance, the operator told him there was none.

Finally in the late afternoon the operator got up from his desk with a paper in hand and shuffled over to the window, and called, "Mr. Collins!"

Breslin almost tore the paper from his hands. After all the strain, he felt his muscles sag. Everything was in order. Under the Devoy code, the message meant that to the best of Captain Anthony's knowledge the mission of the *Catalpa* had not been revealed to or suspected by any English authorities. The Captain waited his arrival in Bunbury.

"Thank you," he remembered to say to the operator, and remembered, too, to give him a crown to wipe the scowl off his face. In two steps he was out of the door and on his way to the Emerald Isle.

He pounded on the door of King's room at the hotel. King opened the door, his face half-lathered, half-shaved. "What's up?" he asked in alarm.

"The ship's arrived! Get that lather off your face and ride like hell for Perth! Tell Desmond to get ready to leave at a moment's notice."

Within twenty minutes, King was galloping for Perth on the fastest horse Albert had in his stables.

Breslin, scarcely losing a stride, hurried to the stagecoach office. Was there a seat available on the Thursday run to Bunbury? The agent was doubtful. A gold piece glittered on the counter. Come to think of it, there might be a seat, yes, there definitely would be a seat available. Breslin paid for it on the spot.

His luck held. Foley was in his room, readying himself for supper.

"Will," Breslin said, "I have the news the boys have been waiting for. You must take a note to Wilson. And it won't be long before you'll be treading the green grass of Ireland."

Hurriedly he scribbled: "Our friend has reached port with greetings from Old Erin. He wishes you all well and hopes you are always amenable to your warders. He hopes to see you soon."

12 . A Barrel of Rotten Pork

Captain Anthony was in a quandary. He didn't know Breslin by
sight, and, by the same token, Breslin didn't know him.

The earliest mail coach Breslin could make left Fremantle on
Thursday morning and was due at Bunbury at four in the afternoon of Friday. Anthony was sure Breslin would waste no time in
securing passage on it. When the coach arrived—well, he'd just
have to look sharp at the passengers, pick out the most likely one,
and trust to luck.

At five minutes past four the coach rattled dustily up to Spencer's Hotel.

Four passengers alighted from seats inside. One climbed down
from the box alongside the driver. He was a slight man in country clothes, and Anthony dismissed him immediately. Of the other
four, one was in regimentals. That eliminated him. Anthony
looked sharply at the other three.

There was his man, he was certain. He was big and he had a
full beard. He was stylishly dressed in a light suit, from which
he fastidiously flicked the dust with an expensive leather glove.
A tall hat topped his head, a gold watch chain spanned his vest.
He looked rich and important.

Anthony stepped down from the hotel porch and addressed the
imposing-looking stranger with a slight rising inflection: "Mr.
Collins!"

Breslin hesitated not a second. The seafaring man before him
had "Yankee" written all over his face. "Captain Anthony!" he
said, smiling broadly as if he had known the mariner all his life.

Captain Anthony led the way to the hotel desk. "My owner,

150

Mr. Collins," he told the clerk. "He will have one of your best rooms for . . ." and he turned to Breslin.

"For the night, at least," Breslin supplied. "As soon as I have freshened up after that bone-racking journey I will be happy to have you as my guest for supper."

Anthony bowed.

They had a generous meal. Then, the evening being fair, they set out for a stroll around the town. Anthony guided their steps to the wooden jetty on the harbor front and led Breslin a safe distance out on the wharf. Breslin grabbed Anthony's hand. "Ah, Captain! Thanks be to God you are here! You'll never know how worried I've been—indeed, all of us have been—when the days and the weeks slipped by with no word from you."

"We had our worries too," Anthony smiled. "We had some storms the like of which I've never seen in all my seafaring days."

"Never mind the past. You're here and everything's all right," Breslin exclaimed.

Anthony shook his head. "I'd like to be able to go along with you on that, but I've trouble enough."

"Trouble?"

"First, my bottom's bad fouled. I know we can't take the time to careen and scrape her. Then I lost a lot of sails in the storms we had. There isn't enough time to have new ones cut here. And I haven't taken any oil—not enough to waste hoops on casks."

Breslin was relieved. "We didn't hire you to take whales, Captain," he said. "All we asked was that you get the *Catalpa* here to Bunbury. That you have done. The oil casks——"

"You don't rightly understand, Mr. Breslin. I know the oil in our hold don't matter. But my crew figure they won't get enough money to buy plug tobacco at the end of the voyage. They're mad. I can trust only the men in my own whaleboat. I got three men in irons aboard ship right now. I got one man in jail in Bunbury. They tried to jump ship. I tell you, my crew is near mutiny."

"I guess I can't help you there, Captain. But the man who brought this bark here against storms, I'm sure can bring his crew into line, no matter how mutinous."

"I'll have your ship ready for you when you want her. No crew ever got the advantage of George Anthony yet. Now, I've spilled my troubles. What about yours?"

"So far, things seem all right," Breslin said cautiously. "Our men are all working within the walls or right outside the prison. None of them are on bush gangs. If they all continue just as they are now, we can get them out of the prison and to the beach I've picked out."

"Tell me about the beach."

"I think it is all right, and so does Father McCabe. It is far enough away from Fremantle so that you can land without being suspected, and close enough for us to reach with galloping horses before pursuit catches up with us. If it doesn't suit you, then we'll try to find another."

"All right, so your beach suits me. Then what?"

"I propose that you have the *Catalpa* stand by outside territorial waters, under light sails, and that you bring your whaleboat to this beach, under darkness, if that is possible . . ."

"Landing on a strange shore after dark and trying to hit one spot? I don't quite like that."

"Then land in twilight. We'll get our men to the spot early next morning. From the beach to the point where your bark would be in neutral waters is about sixteen miles. How long would that take to row?"

Anthony calculated briefly. "About five hours, if the weather is good and there isn't too much of a sea running. I hope we can use the sail. I have a good boat crew, though. They can do it in that time without sail. But I'd like to see the coast between here and Fremantle."

"I was going to recommend taking the steamer back to Fremantle. The government boat, the *Georgette*, is due here tomorrow. She carries the colonial mails. We can engage passage on her, you can reconnoiter the coast and you can visit Fremantle. You're one of my captains—I'm a rich Yankee, you know." Breslin laughed. "You can come back here to Bunbury and get the *Catalpa* ready. I want to make the break by Thursday next week, April 6."

Captain Anthony pursed his lips. "That's mighty close figuring. With the men in irons, I'm shorthanded for getting water and stores aboard. And I can't abandon that man in jail. I'll have to pay his fine, but I'll need every able-bodied hand if it comes to a fight. I'll do my best."

Breslin hustled aboard the *Georgette* Saturday morning with Captain Anthony in tow. He presented the Yankee skipper as "The master of one of my ships—just in from America." He demanded the best accommodations aboard from the purser—accommodations befitting the "Yankee Trader," part of whose get-rich schemes now seemed on the point of fruition.

Anthony found a kindred spirit in Captain Grady, master of the *Georgette*. Grady had once sailed as mate on a London-New York merchantman. By the time the *Georgette* had cleared the harbor the *Catalpa* master was in the pilot house, talking about the coast, courses, bearings, Australian winds and storms. Sunday morning he used Grady's spyglass to study the shoreline around Garden Island, Rottenest and Rockingham.

As Grady eased his ship through Owen Anchorage toward Fremantle's Victoria Quay, both Anthony and Breslin saw at the same time the British gunboat moored to the opposite side of the quay.

The armed craft meant little to Anthony, but Breslin stiffened in horror. The gunboat swarmed with sailors and the muzzles of her guns poked menacingly from ports. As the *Georgette* eased into her berth, Breslin made out the name on the warship's fantail: H.M.S. *Conflict*. There could be no prison break while that heavily armed Royal Navy vessel was in Fremantle. It would be suicide to think of standing up to her guns in a chase.

Breslin whispered his despair to Anthony as the two walked to the Emerald Isle. All Anthony could offer was that he would go back to the waterfront later and try to find out something about the gunboat. He returned from his spying expedition with bad news.

"She has two guns and a crew of thirty," he reported. "She's schooner rigged and everyone says she's mighty fast. We'd be goners if she ever took out after the *Catalpa* in light winds. Maybe

153

in real heavy weather we could show our heels—just maybe."

"Did you find out how long she'll be here?"

"About eight or nine days. Then she may sail to Adelaide in South Australia or to Darwin in the Northern Territory. All the dockwallopers know is that she goes one way or the other each time she visits here."

"Well, we'll just have to sit tight . . ." Breslin began.

"You haven't heard the worst of it. There's another gunboat due to take the colonial governor on a tour of towns in the north part of West Australia. I couldn't find out when she's coming or when she's leaving."

"Then the break's off, for now," Breslin decided with a heavy heart. "We'll have to wait until the *Conflict* is gone and until we find out when the other vessel is due."

They ate a troubled lunch together. Then Breslin brightened. They need not waste all the time. This would be a grand opportunity for the Captain to visit the beach Father McCabe and he had picked out.

Breslin ordered up the matched team he had found on previous occasions to be the best Albert had in his stables, and brought them out onto the sand of the beach in two hours, twenty minutes.

Anthony looked around critically. The beach was well sheltered from the open sea by Garden Island, a long low stretch of land covered by tall grass and bush. At the north end of the island there was a narrow passage to the sea.

"Here is where we expect to deliver our men," Breslin said.

Captain Anthony looked about to fix landmarks. A tall gum tree served for a mark that could be seen from a couple of miles off shore. With Breslin's help he dragged two driftwood logs above high water mark and set them up in the sand as guides. He stood off and looked at them. Then he said solemnly, "These logs mark the place where I will meet you with my boat if God spares my life."

"Amen!" Breslin added.

They devised code messages to cover the new situation presented by the presence of the warship. When the *Conflict* had cleared, Breslin would send this message: "Your friend N. (or S.) has gone home. When do you sail?" Captain Anthony would interpret this to mean: "The gunboat has sailed north (or south). Start from Bunbury." In the event the gunboat that was to take Governor Robinson to the northwest arrived, the message would be: "Jones is going overland to Champion Bay. When do you clear out of Bunbury?" Then, when the coast was clear again, the message would read: "Jones has gone to Champion Bay. Did not receive a letter from you." Then the Captain would get under way.

Back aboard the *Catalpa* after a wearying hundred-mile journey by stage, Captain Anthony told the First Mate all that had transpired.

"When we'll leave, I don't know. That gunboat could stay there a couple of days or a couple of weeks. They didn't seem to be doing any big work on her, just normal port jobs. Until she goes, Breslin will just have to haul his anchors short and wait. The *Conflict* could catch us before we got half our canvas spread. She's a pretty schooner, and you can bet she has a good British Navy crew aboard.

"Now there's no reason for me to stay on shore. I'm going to take charge of building cabins for the Fenians when we get them on board. I want you to get our water and our provisions in the hold as soon as you can. I think you can trust your own boat crew. Farnham can take my boat. Last thing to bring aboard is wood. We could pinch along on what we got."

"How about word from Breslin?" Sam asked.

"Every time you go ashore one of your jobs will be to call at the telegraph office. Got a mighty pretty girl operator there. Mebbe Amy Chase'll have a rival here down-under."

Smith shook his head vehemently.

"Don't be too sure. Beatrice Warren's her name. I found that out for you."

Beatrice might have been the most beautiful girl in Australia, but Sam Smith had another image in his heart. The first thing he did when he took a water cask crew ashore Saturday morning was visit the shop of the jeweler and watchmaker. After a long and careful inspection he bought a heart-shaped brooch made of Australian gold for his Amy Chase. He could just see her eyes light up at the shining trinket.

The water casks were filled by Saturday night. In the steerage, Captain Anthony pushed his men building the additional cabins. To their mutterings about taking up cask space for such things, he said shortly: "We're taking some passengers back to the States. You men'll get your share in the passage money." This was all right with the crew. It was better than flensing whales.

By Monday night all provisions were aboard. Sam had made several trips to the telegraph office, where Beatrice had engaging smiles for the husky Yankee but no messages for the master of the *Catalpa*.

Anthony went ashore to secure the release of Coeking, still a prisoner of the Water Police. It cost the Captain two English pounds to settle the assault charges. When Coeking had been taken back on the *Catalpa*, he was put in irons with the three other deserters.

Breslin haunted the waterfront. The *Conflict*'s captain seemed to be in no hurry to get under way. From the prison Foley brought heartbreaking news.

"Red Darragh, he do be cryin'," Foley told Breslin. "He says they ain't never gettin' outa the prison. And Jim Wilson says he's about give up. He's fer breakin' out and cuttin' and runnin' for it. I told him to take it easy for a spell. All of 'em, they's just fair breaking with the waitin'."

Tuesday morning, April 11, when Breslin made his visit to the quay, the *Conflict* was gone. Waterfront hands told him she had sailed south, likely for Adelaide. No one had any idea when the other gunboat would arrive.

Breslin took a long chance. Over the wires went the message: "Your Friend S. has gone home. When do you sail?" If all was well, he reckoned, the *Catalpa* should get under way that very afternoon and the rescue could be made Thursday morning, April 13.

All day he waited, scarcely daring to leave the telegraph office. No reply came. The telegraph operator, surly over Breslin's constant queries, slammed the message window shut, locked the office and stomped off. Breslin went to bed puzzled, unhappy, worried sick.

Tuesday morning Sam made another trip ashore to secure firewood and a few remaining items for the ship. He made his usual trip to the telegraph office.

"Anything for the *Catalpa,* Miss Warren?" he asked.

"Ah, Yank, why can't you call me Bea? I'd call you by your first name, if I knew it." She eyed him archly.

"Well—it's Sam, if you must know," he retorted.

"Now that's more like it, Sam. I wanted to ask you to go on a picnic on Sunday—after church, of course. That's Easter Sunday. Some of us are going up river and we're going to have the last picnic of the season."

Sam lifted his eyebrows and shrugged. "Well now, if we don't sail . . ."

"You tell your old captain not to sail until we have our picnic," Bea insisted.

"You tell the old man. He'd chew my head off."

"Maybe I will. Do him good to get told off," Bea said. "If he says he'll wait, then will you go?"

"Could be. Now, is there anything for the ship?"

"Come to think of it, there is." She handed him a telegram.

Sam grabbed it.

"Don't rush off so——"

But Sam was out of the door and on the way to the bark before she could get out another word.

Captain Anthony read Breslin's wire. The ship was ready. All he needed was port clearance. He ordered his boat overside.

Ashore he started the tedious procedure of obtaining official clearance for the *Catalpa.* Customs men were dispatched to the bark to search her for stowaways and for contraband material. At the customs office he signed interminable papers and, after a final snarl of red tape, secured all his necessary papers.

Heaving a sigh of relief, Captain Anthony started back to the dock, but he hadn't taken a dozen steps before a harried customs man ran after him.

"You cannot sail, Captain!" he announced breathlessly. "I have just had word from our men at the quay. They have placed your vessel in custody."

The bewildered Captain hurried out to his ship. Sam was sitting dejectedly on a hatch cover. Some of the *Catalpa* crew lolled around grinning expectantly. A uniformed customs officer sat beside the First Mate.

"What's up, Sam?" Captain Anthony asked.

"This officer here says we landed a barr'l of pork from the bark and didn't pay duty."

"Did we?"

"You recollect the barr'l. 'Tweren't fit to eat. I give it to the hotel man. He said 'twas fitten only for the pigs and that's where 'twould go."

"I can't give you clearance," the customs officer said firmly. "You'll have to go back to the customs house and argue it out there. Meantime, this ship is legally detained by Her Majesty. I am her representative."

Captain Anthony rowed ashore gloomily. All this pother over a mess of rotten pork. If he had his way, all customs men—and the pork—would be fed to the sharks and the sooner the better.

The arguments consumed hours, finally entailing an official visit to the proprietor of Spencer's Hotel, who confirmed the Captain's story. The customs men were at last convinced that the pork had not been fit for human consumption, that it had indeed been presented to a pig farmer. The *Catalpa* could proceed.

A whole day lost. Breslin must be frantic. Anthony hurried to the telegraph office. It was shut tight.

Breslin didn't sleep a wink all night. He tossed and turned, got up, looked out the window at the silent town, went back to bed to toss some more. What in God's name was delaying the answer from Anthony? Haggard and worn, Wednesday morning he once more went to the telegraph office.

The operator gave him a curt good morning and turned to his telegraphic apparatus. Message after message poured in, government business taking precedence. Finally, just as Breslin had about given up hope, the word he had been waiting for clicked in. "I sail today. Good-by. Answer if received. Anthony."

Breslin's knees went weak. If Anthony left Bunbury that day, he would be off Rockingham beach Friday morning. Friday was Good Friday. Not only was it a church holy day but it was a government holiday too. All government buildings would be closed. The telegraph offices in Fremantle and in Bunbury would be shut down. There would be no work parties of prisoners. All of them would be confined to the Establishment, for church services and for an infrequent day of rest.

With trembling fingers, Breslin scribbled a message to the *Catalpa*. The telegraph key buzzed. Breslin clutched his rosary. If only the Blessed Virgin would grant him this one boon—that Captain Anthony would wait indeed, as he had said, to get this answer.

Captain Anthony waited ashore Wednesday morning for an answer to his sailing message. The harbor officials he gammed with about the weather were pessimistic. Though the winds were steady at the moment, they predicted a swing to the northwest during the late afternoon or the night.

"Captain," his informant warned, "if the wind holds in the northwest for a couple of hours, it will blow hard. If the wind then swings to the south and abates, you'll have fair sailing. But if the wind swings back into the northwest again, then batten down, you're in for it."

Bea, with a saucy smile, handed him Breslin's message shortly before noon. It read: "Your telegram received. Friday being Good Friday I shall remain at Fremantle and start for York on Saturday morning. I wish you may strike oil. Collins."

Captain Anthony could have kicked himself for not realizing

the holy day was at hand. He could only blame that infernal argument over a mess of spoiled pork. He dashed off a telegram in reply and gave it to Bea.

In Fremantle, Breslin ate a hasty lunch, then haunted the telegraph office again. One o'clock came and went. Two o'clock. Four o'clock. He couldn't give a final alert to Desmond or to the men in prison. Time enough when he had something definite. King agreed.

Five o'clock and the reply came. "Yours received. Did not sail today. Winds ahead and rising. Sailing in morning. Good-by. Anthony."

The *Catalpa* would be off Rockingham Saturday morning! Breslin shed his worries and his depression as he would a tattered coat. Now was the time for fast, final action.

First, he alerted Desmond. He scribbled a telegram. "I leave for York Saturday." That code message would bring Desmond to Fremantle Friday night with his matched team, a wagonette, the clothes, the guns and the ammunition.

Now, word to the prisoners.

It was late. Work parties were already back in the prison. Tomorrow, the holy day, all would be confined within the Establishment. It would be impossible for him to give Wilson the signal—right forefinger laid along the nose, then moved across the right cheek: "Get ready! We start tomorrow."

Foley must take one more chance. He must smuggle just one more note behind the walls. He must find some way to get into the prison on Good Friday. Then he could start for his beloved Ireland.

At Foley's lodgings, Breslin penned his note on a bit of paper, tiny enough so it could be swallowed instantly: "Our friends are ready. They will be at the place Saturday morning. Obey Wilson in everything he orders. He is the leader. We have money, guns, clothes. Let no man's heart fail him. This chance can never come again. Erin go bragh."

"Will," Breslin said gravely, "this note to Wilson means life or death. Get it to him—then sail for Ireland with the blessings of the Clan upon you."

Will replied just as gravely. "I'll get the note to Jim first thing Friday morning."

Breslin hurried back to the Emerald Isle, jubilant at last. Everything was in hand. He slept lightly. At midnight he was awakened by a deluge of rain dashing against the window panes. He rose and looked out. Torrents of rain swept the deserted street, driven by a wind that seemed to mount in ferocity with each gust. If this storm lashed the whole coast, the *Catalpa* might be in serious trouble. "Oh, God," he thought, "how many more disappointments can come to me?"

For the rest of the night he lay sleepless, listening to the tempest—the roar of the rain and the snarl of the wind.

Early Thursday afternoon, Captain Anthony went ashore to make certain no more red tape stood between his ship and port clearance.

Back on the bark, he looked at the barometer. At the noon reading, the mercury had stood at a trifle over thirty inches. Now, only three hours later, the column had dropped a full inch and a half. The sky was darkening, and a fresh breeze from the northwest whipped the bay water into whitecaps.

By nightfall, a wicked wind was lashing the harbor. The Captain ordered the royal and topgallant yards sent down and snugged the *Catalpa* for foul weather. The anchor cables were payed out full to ease the strain. She should ride the blow, he figured, and went below.

Shortly before eleven o'clock, Bolles, who had the night watch, called the Captain. The ship was taking heavy punishment in a wind that was full northwest and nearing gale force.

As the weatherwise ashore had foretold, the wind began to shift to the south. The barometer showed a drop of another half inch to twenty-eight. The wind held south until two in the morning, quieted momentarily, then switched sharply back to northwest.

Smothering rain squalls chased across the white-lathered water as dawn broke. Huge seas roared down on the ship, cascading her decks. Again and again she smashed her bow so deep that solid green water sluiced over the forward deck, crashed against the tryworks and flooded the waist.

First Mate Sam Smith came on duty with the midwatch, stood beside Anthony watching the strain on the anchor cables, now rigid as iron bars.

"Another hour and she'll drag," Anthony said. "If the anchors let go, we'll pile up on the beach. Get all our people on deck. We'll have to work fast to save her if the anchors don't hold!"

"*All hands!*" brought grim-faced seamen to their posts, port watch at foremast, starboard watch at main and mizzen. The Captain told off a second man at the wheel.

The wind howled up to hurricane force and there was a lash of coming winter in the bitter blasts. The *Catalpa* smashed hawse-pipe deep. A giant wall of water raced the full length of her, soaking every man. The bark shuddered, then reared like a crazy stallion. There was a sudden lurch. Then another.

"She's draggin'!" Smith yelled.

"Set tops'ls!" Captain Anthony bawled.

Men monkey-raced into the rigging, loosed the sopping canvas to the gale. The big topsails slatted, then slapped thunderously belly-tight.

"Fore tops'ls aback!" Anthony shouted.

The ship lurched again as the four tons of anchors lost their grip on the sand and mud bottom. The great yard was hauled about and sheeted home.

Sam looked nervously at Captain Anthony, who stood rain-drenched, fists clenched.

The drawing main topsail, giving the bark headway against the gale, should be balanced by the backed fore topsail. The ship should hold almost stationary. The anchors should get a chance to bite deep into new holding ground.

The bark plunged again. Green water sluiced her deck. Another sickening lurch meant a new slip and slide along the harbor bed. The shore was a scant two cable lengths away. Again she plunged and lurched, but on the next smash into a giant white-maned wave the bark rose steady.

"She's holding, Sam!"

It was well past dawn when the wind began to abate almost as fast as it had made up. The sun broke through the ragged edges of the clouds but the seas ran heavy, and the now contrary wind made it certain that the *Catalpa* could not clear for Rockingham that day. Even if she set sail now, she could not be off the rescue beach soon enough to keep the whaleboat rendezvous. Breslin would have to be notified at once.

Anthony went below and thumbed through the code book. Not a single message would take care of the situation. He dipped pen in ink and struggled to put together words that would tell Breslin of the delay, yet not alarm him too much. Finally he decided on: "It has blown heavy. Ship dragged both anchors. Can you advance more money if needed. Will telegraph you again in the morning."

Breslin should realize that a ship dragging her anchors wasn't in much trouble. He would certainly translate "more money" as more time. "Telegraph in the morning" should tell him everything could go ahead as planned with a day of delay.

It was past noon before a boat could be launched without swamping. Sam carried the message for Breslin tucked in the pocket of his pea jacket.

Captain Anthony stayed aboard to get necessary repairs made and to prepare for sailing in the morning. He set the carpenter to work and ordered the royal and topgallant yards hoisted again.

Ashore, Sam raced for the telegraph office. It was closed. A grinning native, eying his salt-stained pants and shoes, called: "It's a holiday, Yank—Good Friday." He chuckled at Sam's look of dismay.

"Where's Miss Warren?"

"Like as not home taking a beauty nap."

"Can I get her down to the telegraph office?"

"Not a chance, Yank, not a chance. Not Bea Warren."

Sam ran to Bea's house and pounded on the door.

"Why, Sam Smith! How nice!" Bea answered his thunderous summons. "But you didn't have to knock the door down. I'd have come if you'd just whispered."

She held the door open invitingly. As Sam hesitated, she said, a little more insistently: "Your shoes are sopping. Come into the kitchen and dry them."

Sam entered the hallway. "Bea——" he began.

"Why, Sam Smith! That's the very first time you ever called me Bea, I do believe," she said happily.

"Look, Bea, I can't stay. I got a telegram my Captain says has got to be sent today . . ."

Bea tittered. "Oh, bother your old Captain. Let him hire a pigeon to carry his message. You come on back in the kitchen and take those wet shoes off. I'll fix something hot." She blushed. "Momma and Poppa are out."

Sam shook his head doggedly. "Thank you, Bea, but I want you to open the office. Please!"

"Work on a holiday? If I didn't think you were so nice—for a Yank—I'd say you were daft. Me work on a holiday? Who ever heard of such a thing?"

"Look, Bea . . ."

Bea tossed her flaxen head. "Even if I had a mind to go to the office—which I haven't—I couldn't get anyone on the wire."

"Isn't the Fremantle station open?"

"The Fremantle and Perth stations are always open," Bea admitted grudgingly, "on account of the prison and the governor and so on. But they'll only take government stuff."

"Couldn't you try?"

"Why should I, Yank? It's cozy here. You haven't even promised for sure you'll come to my picnic on Sunday."

"I will, so help me, I will," Sam promised.

"Your old Captain won't let you," Bea said archly.

"Then I'll jump ship, so help me, I will. Now, please, come on!"

"How can I depend on you?" Bea eyed him narrowly.

"Look!" Sam reached into the inner pocket of his jacket, and pulled out the gold brooch he had bought for Amy Chase. "Look! I was goin' to give it to you at the picnic. Don't that show I was goin' to take you?"

Bea's eyes snapped in pleasure. "My," she said. "It is pretty! Thank you, Sam."

"Now will you try to get someone on the telegraph?"

165

"Oh, all right."

At the office she tapped out the code for Fremantle. "Dot dash dot space dot pause dot dot—for 'FR.'" There was no answer.

"I told you there isn't any use. Let's go back to the house."

"Try again! Please keep on trying!"

Halfheartedly she tapped her key again.

This time the sounder clicked.

"He says 'GA BU' . . . that's 'Go ahead, Bunbury.' I'll ask him if he'll take a message."

The key rattled and the sounder clicked.

"He'll only take an emergency message, he says."

"This is a matter of life or death," Sam implored. "Tell him that!"

The telegraph instruments chattered madly.

Bea said: "He'll take it. Give me the message."

That Friday morning, Breslin felt as if he had been personally buffeted by the storm that had raged all night. He sloshed his face with cold water and went down to breakfast.

There was a message for him at the desk: "Foley says he delivered the goods and they were received in good condition. P. McC."

Breslin smiled in satisfaction. The day was starting well after all. This should be the last they all would ever see of this hateful part of the world. The men knew tomorrow was "the Day."

He walked up the hill to Good Friday Mass. The air was as fresh and bracing as a breeze over the green fields of Ireland.

Father McCabe intoned the solemn Mass of the Pre-Sanctified with tremendous dignity and feeling. Breslin could sense that the good father was striving, in his words and in his tone and in his prayers, to give his blessing to the perilous undertaking that lay ahead. In nearby pews were the others who were deep in the plot—King and Walsh and McCarthy and wispy Foley.

After the service, Breslin walked slowly toward the Emerald Isle. The others caught up with him. He ran through a last-minute check of plans with them.

"Foley! What of the men?"

"All got jobs nearby all week. Wilson's on the dock. He says all right. They be ready."

"King! Hire your horse today. Be ready to follow Desmond and me when we start out. Wait until nine o'clock. Watch out for an alarm. Then ride fast after us."

"Right!"

"Walsh! McCarthy! You have your nippers? Walsh, you cut the telegraph wires on the Bunbury road. McCarthy, take care of the wires to Perth. I want the wires cut at exactly eight o'clock, and I want them wrecked so it will take hours to fix them." He grinned at their answering nods. "All right now, let's split up and walk along. See you all in the morning."

After lunch Breslin ordered his usual matched pair at Albert's and drove them out the Perth Road to see they were in condition. Back at the stable in mid-afternoon, he left strict orders that the same team must be harnessed to a light wagonette for use at seven o'clock next morning. A crown tip to the hostler brought a quick "Yessir, Mr. Collins."

As he walked back to the hotel he saw Desmond drive by with a beautiful team of chestnuts behind a wagonette. An almost imperceptible nod from Breslin told Desmond all was well.

Breslin continued on to the hotel. On the porch he chatted awhile with other guests, then entered the lobby.

A telegram was waiting for him. He did not question how it had been sent and received on the Holy Day, his eyes saw only the dire words:

"It has blown heavy. Ship dragged both anchors. Can you advance more money if needed? Will telegraph you again in the morning."

Breslin turned gray. Beads of sweat stood out on his forehead. The hotel clerk looked at him with concern.

"Is it bad news, Mr. Collins? Can I be of service?"

"No . . . no . . . yes . . . bad news . . . I'll be all right. . . ."

He almost staggered up the stairs to his room, to slump into a chair.

167

This message was no prearranged code. Something had gone terribly wrong.

It was the storm. The *Catalpa* must have gone aground, her planking stove in, her timbers cracked. There would be weeks of delay. She must need repairs badly. Else why the words: "Can you advance more money?" Anthony had been told their funds were running low. Where could he and Desmond or King or Walsh or McCarthy put their hands on more gold now? How could he stay on in Fremantle, suspect as he must be right now?

Then, the first shock over, he began to rationalize. Perhaps this was an improvised code message. "Can you advance more money?" Could not that mean "Can you give me a little more time to make minor repairs?" The message did not say there had been any extensive damage to the ship itself. "Ship dragged both anchors." Even if the anchors had been lost, if the captain had had to cut their cables, new ones could be readily procured in Bunbury. "Will telegraph you again in the morning." Surely that meant that no serious damage had been done.

But even if Anthony sailed in the morning—Saturday—the rescue attempt must be postponed until Monday. Everyone must be notified immediately to stand by until further orders.

Breslin took a deep breath, and walked downstairs outwardly composed. The clerk looked at him admiringly. That Mr. Collins was a cool one—got bad news, bounced right back again. A cool one.

Desmond was at the hotel bar. Breslin stood alongside him. "Go back to Perth, Tom. Something's gone wrong with the ship. Wait the word!"

King was still in his room. Breslin told him about the message.

McCarthy and Walsh next. Breslin tried not to appear excited as he walked to their modest lodging house. He dawdled along, looking at shop windows, only hurrying his footsteps after he had reached the corner of their street. They took the news mournfully.

Foley would have to get into the prison once more and tell the men the rescue was off until further word. He'd have to hurry to get inside the gates on some errand pretext before they were shut for the night.

Breslin knocked on the door. Foley's landlady answered.

"Will? He ain't here. He went out. I don't rightly know where. Said some friends was giving him a going away party. He's for Ireland soon."

Breslin felt sick and frustrated. He could not blame Foley—everything had been in hand when they had met at church that very morning. But Wilson and the rest had to be warned, else they would make a premature break on the morrow.

"Only a miracle . . ." Breslin thought. Suddenly prayer seemed right and proper—and the only hope. Surely God would be merciful. He walked to the church.

The sanctuary lamp and a few votive candles added their tiny light to the dying rays of the afternoon sun. Black covered the altar in memory of the crucified Christ.

Breslin began to make the Stations of the Cross. With each supplication he added a fervent prayer to the Virgin that somehow, some way, she would help him in his trouble. After the fourteenth Station he felt spiritually at peace for the first time in days. He did not doubt for a moment that there would be an answer to his prayers.

As he turned to the door, he saw, framed in the sunset glow, one of the men he most wanted to see—Martin Hogan. He grabbed the startled, gloom-blinded prisoner by the arm and pulled him into a pew. "Martin! I asked for a miracle. The Blessed Virgin Mary has given it to me. How on earth did you happen here?"

"Just another errand to Father McCabe. I figured I'd not be missed if I took the time to make the Stations."

"Martin, we can't get away tomorrow!"

The saber cuts across Hogan's bronzed cheek stood out white. "You promised, John Breslin!" he lashed. "You said everything was ready. You said the ship was here. You said you had the guns."

"Don't get excited," Breslin soothed. "Everything is just as it was. The ship is at hand but she's had trouble. She dragged her anchors in the storm. She was hurt some too."

Hogan nodded. "Ah, that storm! We feared it might do hurt to the ship."

"It can't be serious. The captain said he'd telegraph me in the morning. Now, make your Stations, pray hard, then go back and tell the boys they'll have to be patient. Tell them I'll give the signal myself to the first one I see. You know it." He put his right forefinger alongside his nose, then drew it across his right cheek. "That means 'tomorrow.' See that all of the boys know it."

"For God's sake, hurry," Hogan said. "They're talking about building a new road. You know what that will mean!"

"There won't be a minute wasted."

Breslin felt as if a weight had been lifted from his shoulders. Now, if things were only going well on the *Catalpa* . . . The morrow would surely tell.

By Saturday morning the wind had gentled fresh from the west, and the clouds gave way.

Captain Anthony ordered his boat overside and went ashore, first to reassure the port authorities that the only reason he had delayed his departure was because of the storm, and second, to send the word to Breslin that at last all was ready at his end.

He gave Bea this message for Breslin: "I shall certainly leave Bunbury for the whaling grounds today. Suppose you and your friends start for York Monday morning. Good-by. Anthony."

After lunch at the Spencer he went back to the telegraph office. His reply was waiting—along with a black look from Bea because her picnic with Sam now was ruined.

Breslin's wire said: "Your telegram received. All right. Glad you got off without damage. I wish you would strike oil. Au revoir. J. Collins."

Anthony returned to the bark. Conditions were good. The breeze was now moderate from the southwest, the skies were clear, the weather pleasant and the barometer rising. The *Catalpa* took her anchors aboard. One fluke of the big two-ton port anchor was gone, broken off when the bark dragged.

The bark stood to sea.

Breslin could not risk another telegram to Desmond. He dispatched King to Perth as soon as he had received the message from Anthony that the *Catalpa* was sailing. Walsh and McCarthy got their instructions all over again and a last warning: "I want those telegraph lines really wrecked!"

As unconcernedly as he could Breslin strolled to the jetty, and walked out on the tarred planks, puffing on an important-looking cigar, pausing to look at the fleecy clouds, stopping to puzzle out the play of the little fish around the salty piles, inching ever nearer to the convict timber-loading party.

Now he was abreast of the convicts. He could see that Wilson had spotted him, though he kept on working industriously.

Breslin laid his right forefinger alongside the bridge of his nose, then moved it across his right cheek.

A look of disbelief and of disgust darkened Wilson's swarthy face. Tomorrow? Breslin must be mad. How could they start on Sunday? Didn't the man know that there were no work details on Sunday, that every man was penned behind the walls of the Establishment that day—unless he went to church?

Breslin sidled nearer. He took a big pull on his cigar, looked at its fine white ash appreciatively, puffed out the smoke. "Monday!" he murmured, and walked on.

Wilson's slight nod told Breslin he understood.

Easter morning Breslin, King, McCarthy and Walsh attended Mass. At the church door Breslin tarried until Father McCabe came out. Breslin whispered to the priest: "Your blessing, Father. We try in the morning."

"May the Holy Mother protect you all!" Father McCabe's eyes misted. "I'll pray the night for you. Write to me when you get to America."

171

Breslin hurried to rejoin the others and went over his instructions again as they walked along: Walsh and McCarthy slash telegraph lines at eight o'clock; King ride rearguard, start from town at nine and gallop to catch up with Breslin and Desmond in the wagons.

Back at the Emerald Isle Breslin packed a single bag. The rest of his dunnage he would abandon. He went down to the hotel lobby. "Fetch your employer," he said to the obsequious clerk.

Maloney appeared, bowing low. "Yes, Mr. Collins?"

"I shall be away for several days, my man. Keep my room fresh for me."

"Of course, Mr. Collins. And may I ask where you are going?" He saw the look of annoyance on Breslin's face. "Just in case any inquire as to where you may be found."

Breslin froze him with a glance. "If you must know, I shall drive first to Perth."

At about two in the afternoon, while Breslin sat on the hotel porch, Desmond drove in from Perth, sawing viciously at a sorry pair of nags, far different from the well-matched pair he had brought on the false start.

He stabled his team and secured a room. "The devil take these Australian bushwackers," he snorted to Breslin. "The crowbait they gave me! All the way from Perth one of those damn nags wanted to go to Fremantle and the other one wanted to get back to his stable. Between the two of them they'd never beat a turtle in a race from taw. And that thieving Summers got his sovereign, in advance too!"

"But the team you had before?"

"Gone to York, so I was told. Hired just after I brought them back yesterday. I held a pound in front of the hostler for a better pair, but he said they were all spoken for."

"They'll have to do. Tell the stable boy you'll want them hitched up at seven tomorrow morning." Breslin dropped his voice. "Did your bring the goods?"

"They're in the back, covered safe with a blanket," Desmond whispered back.

When Breslin went to Albert's stables to hire the team he had driven so many times, he found that the better horse of the pair had been hired out to Superintendent John Stone of the Water Police. Stone's brother-in-law, the sheriff, had been thrown from his horse and was in critical condition in Perth. At least, Breslin thought wryly, Stone would be ten miles away on Monday morning.

Not only was the team broken up, but Albert told Breslin he doubted if he could have a team for him at all in the morning. The regatta at Perth over the Easter weekend had just about cleaned him out of horses. He hoped there would be some teams returned, but he wasn't promising.

Six rescued men, Desmond, King and himself in one small wagonette behind two of the sorriest nags in Australia! It would take them twice as long to pull to the beach. If the English set out in pursuit, they would catch them before they even got to Ten Mile Well.

The *Catalpa* stood northward along the coast under short canvas all Saturday night. With favoring winds, she was about eight miles offshore and thirty miles southwest of Rottnest lighthouse by Sunday noon. Closer to Fremantle than that, Captain Anthony dared not sail. There was a signal station at the lighthouse from which news of incoming ships was telegraphed to Fremantle. He did not want his arrival tipped off.

In his cabin, Captain Anthony and First Mate Smith had a last talk over a tot of rum and water.

"You got a big job ahead of you, Sam," Anthony said gravely. "Here's what I want you to do: take the ship at least twelve miles offshore and keep her that far out all the time. Always be certain you are well outside Australian territorial waters. That way, the law's on your side at least. The English can't touch you. And don't let them bluff you.

"If everything goes right, we should take the Irishmen off the beach at Rockingham about ten o'clock tomorrow morning. As soon as we get them aboard the whaleboat we'll shove off and head for you. If the wind favors we'll use sail. If it's contrary, then we'll have to pull for it. We should raise you long before dark. Keep lookouts posted in both masts all the time and warn them to look sharp for us. If the Water Police or a gunboat hails you, tell them I've gone ashore to fetch a new anchor to take the place of the one we broke. It wouldn't fool a whaleman, but these English are stupid. Any rate, that's your story and stick to it. They can't arrest you.

"I'm going to say good-by now, Sam. There's a mighty big chance we'll be caught. If we are, I think the crew will get off scot free. They don't know anything about what's going on. As for me—well, I reckon that Fremantle prison has a lot of empty cells. If I don't show up by the time you figure I should, then the ship is yours . . ."

"I'll sail her right in to Fremantle an' demand them swabs turn you loose," Sam interrupted.

"You will not!" Anthony said grimly. "My orders are: if I'm not back the ship is yours. Go whaling. Get the casks full of oil. Make some money for yourself and Amy Chase. And when you get home, tell Emmie what happened. Tell her I'll get home somehow."

He stood up. They clasped hands.

"Good luck, George," Sam said.

"I'll need it!" Anthony said drily. "I'm going to take Farnham with me. If something happens to me, the men will have a good officer to boss them. Maybe they can get back to the ship."

Anthony picked up a heavy coat and climbed on deck, Sam at his heels. The *Catalpa* was idling along.

"Get my boat overside, Mr. Smith," Captain Anthony ordered. "And, cook, get me a couple hams, some hardbread and some water casks. Mr. Farnham, I want you with me."

The Second Mate dutifully slid down the falls.

"You, Big Louie! You, Mopsy and Gingy! You, Tom. You, Ferris. Go below. Get your coats. We'll be gone overnight."

The boat crew scurried below.

174

Sam pressed a bottle of rum on the captain. "Thanks, Sam," Anthony grinned. "I may be needing that."

Captain Anthony gave a last shake of the hand to Sam, then slid down the davit falls after his men. He took the steering oar. "Shove off!"

It was precisely one o'clock Sunday afternoon. The breeze favoring, the Captain ordered the leg-o-mutton sail hoisted and set course for the shore and his secret beachhead. The whaleboat made the southern end of Garden Island in late afternoon. Anthony ordered the sail furled, to lessen the boat's visibility from shore. The men rowed steadily around Cape Peron and the southern end of Cockburn Sound. As they came abreast of Collie Head they were startled by a noise almost as loud as thunder. Farnham spotted the peril. "Breakers ahead!"

Dead ahead huge seas boiled, seemingly from nowhere.

"Trail oars! Trim this damn boat!" Captain Anthony shouted.

The boat was tossed high in the air by three of the huge combers, then settled down in the smoother waters of Mangles Bay.

The men rowed on. It was growing dark. Straining his eyes, Anthony spotted the big gum tree that was his first landmark. The surf was light as they approached the shore. The whaleboat lifted on the swell, then raced shoreward to hiss on the sand. The men were overside in a flash to drag her up on the beach.

Captain Anthony found his markers not two hundred feet away. It was eight-thirty in the evening of Sunday.

After a meal of cold ham and biscuits, washed down with rum and water, the Captain ordered his men to lie down in the beach grass and get some sleep. It was clear and warm and the weary sailors were soon snoring.

Captain Anthony sat quietly, looking out to the dark that was the sea. Overhead was a vast canopy of brilliant stars. In back was the fearsome shadow of the bush and the forest.

He paced along the beach, looking, thinking, waiting.

He could not sleep.

14 . Easter

A sense of complacency hovered about the person of Superintendent Donan as he walked through the parade of the Establishment that Easter Sunday afternoon. His ruddy face actually cracked into a semblance of a smile as he accepted the stiff salutes of the warders. There were a few scattered boos and catcalls from the more troublesome prisoners, but even these seemed to his ears to be given quite halfheartedly.

Superintendent Donan had reason for his feelings of elation. No less a personage than His Excellency Governor Robinson himself had informed him that on the last official inspection the Establishment had been rated very high indeed. It would be the pleasure of His Excellency to recommend that Superintendent Donan be suitably rewarded, possibly in rank, certainly in his stipend.

Superintendent Donan was, in fact, so pleased with himself that he had ordered the prison cooks to prepare a sumptuous holiday repast for his inmates. Instead of the bully beef of common daily fare, there was a whole mutton boiled, with fresh cabbage, newly dug potatoes, and fresh carrots. There was molasses to sweeten the cocoa—which was served piping hot for a change—and plum duff made from native fruits to top off the banquet.

There was a carefree attitude in the great yard after such a magnificent feast. Prisoners gathered under what might well be the last hot sun of the autumn. One group played at bowls, some contrived a cricket match, others formed a hollow square for a boxing match. Another group was earnestly engaged in a game of cards.

No one, least of all Superintendent Donan, took note that the card players were those oft-troublesome Irish political prisoners. Nor did any of the warders note the undercurrent of serious conversation beneath the banter as each hand was played. Nor did any of the guards observe that the greasy slip of paper on which tally was being kept contrasted markedly with the piece of snow-white paper one prisoner slipped to another.

Wilson studied the worn cards in his hand. "Two for me!" he announced. Then, in a whisper: "You got it all straight now, Bob? You play sick tomorrow morning. The medico don't come round till nearly nine. You play you was took bad. You go to the latrine. Then you wander to the gate. The gateman won't know you're on sickcall. You show him that note. It's to the officer in charge of the jetty details. You walk down to the jetty calm-like. You give that note to the officer in charge . . . Your bet, Mike . . . The note calls for you to take Mike and me to the Marine Residence to move some furniture. We follow you . . . Raise it a pound . . . but we walk right along out past the prison and out on the Rockingham road . . ."

"See that raise . . ." Bob studied. "How much time I got?"

"All bets down? Breslin said he'd have the wagons a fast five minutes walk from the prison . . . he'll wait until nine o'clock. . . . Mother of God, what beastly luck! . . . Red, you can make it out easy any time. That Church of England chaplain of yours will believe anything. You tell the warders you have to have Tom Hassett to——"

"To help me plant old Broomhole's potatoes."

A warder sauntered near. They played a new hand in high glee. "Damn you, Bob, if you could cash in your winnin's you could buy the whole shebeen," Wilson complained. The guard walked on. "Martin, you're painting Fauntleroy's house, ain't you?"

Hogan nodded. "I'll stay . . . Right, still on the job."

"Watch for Tom and Red. When you see them, start off after them. Carry your paintbrushes and your pail. Make like you was going someplace else to paint. Then leg it out on the Rockingham road. Got that all straight?"

They played another hand. Wilson had one last word: "Remember, every mother's son of you, like Breslin said, this is our last chance. We'll never get out of this place if we don't make it tomorrow. Breslin says he's all ready. Let's make sure there ain't no slip-ups on our side."

At sunrise, Monday morning, Captain Anthony's crew stomped their feet, finger-raked dried grass out of their hair and waited orders from their Captain. Under his direction, they gathered grass and twigs and started a small fire, broiled slices of ham over the flames, and washed down the meat and hardbread with water from one of the boat casks.

As the morning haze lifted, Anthony saw that they were within a quarter-mile of the Jarrah Timber Company jetty. On his visit to the beach with Breslin, he had reckoned on being much farther away than that. As the whalemen watched, a gang of five men walked out on the jetty and started to work on a timber pile. One of them looked their way, then started toward them along the beach.

"Who be ye?" he demanded suspiciously as he came up to them.

Captain Anthony explained he was master of a whaler, bound to Fremantle for an anchor to replace one lost in the storm.

"An' whar mought this ship o' yourn be?"

"She's standing off shore. I didn't know the coast. We'll row back to her when we've bought the anchor. We stopped here to rest last night when it came dark."

"Look, lad," the man grinned wisely. "Stow that stuff. You've hooked it from some ship. You better get goin'. This ain't no place to hide. You be deserters."

"Like hell we are!"

"Mebbe you're after someone?"

"I told you why I'm here. Ask any of the men if we didn't lose an anchor. Ask them who's Captain."

Finally satisfied, the man introduced himself as William Ball and turned friendly enough. He gave Anthony some bad news. Ball and his men were there to load some timber on the government ship *Georgette*. When was she due? Matter of hours, Ball said.

If the *Georgette* arrived and Ball told Captain Grady about the Yankee who was fool enough to row for an anchor, then the *Catalpa* master was going to run into some fancy questioning.

Ball turned to leave. Then, as an afterthought, he said: "Watch out when you leave, Captain. Keep close to Garden Island. There's a hell of a reef a bit outside. You'll get wrecked sure."

"But that's the way I came in last night!"

"Then the Lord had you in His hand," Ball said solemnly. He shook hands and walked back to the jetty.

The *Catalpa* men were scared.

"Cap'n, him fella t'row dis fella in jail?" Mopsy asked tearfully.

"Him won't," Captain Anthony said firmly. "No one you fellas is going to be thrown in jail. He knows we're not deserters. No one will hurt you."

The men continued to mutter. The Captain decided that in spite of his original decision not to divulge the real reason for the stop on the beach, a little of the truth might be well used now.

"Look, you men! I said we were going to pick up some passengers in New Zealand and they'd pay gold for passage to the States? I promised you'd all get some of that gold for your lay? Well, those men have changed their minds. I had word they want to be picked up off this beach today instead of in New Zealand. They're prospectors and they're in the woods now. They will be here soon. When they come—they'll likely be in wagons—I want to get them on board ship as soon as we can sail or row them there. When I give you the order to shove off I want every man to look alive, get this boat off the beach like the Old Harry was after us and row like hell for the ship! Mister Farnham, fetch me the bottle. We'll have a bit of rum to wash the vittles down."

Easter Monday dawned fair and cool in Fremantle. For the townspeople, it promised to be a busy day. At the site of the new Freemason's Hall, a flag-draped speakers' stand, bearing a beautiful medallion of Her Most Gracious Majesty Queen Victoria, waited to accommodate the notables from far and wide who would attend, with hundreds of others, the cornerstone laying.

At Victoria Quay lay the government ship *Georgette,* thin blue smoke lazily lifting from her funnel. Captain Grady had spent the holiday and the night ashore. Her crew slumbered, some peacefully, some soddenly, in her forecastle. Her officers snoozed in more elegant berths. She needed more coal to fill her bunkers, but this would go into her holds before she sailed on her regular mail run this very day.

At the Establishment the day began, as usual, with reveille at five—long before the sun had peeped above the autumnal horizon. Breakfast followed, then came parade inspection and assignment of the prisoners to work parties for the day.

Along the road to Bunbury trudged a solitary figure, a bundle over his shoulder, at the end of a stout stick. He lifted his feet wearily. The road was long and lonesome. On the highway to Perth, a similar walker plodded along. In each of the bundles was just one object of note—heavy wire-cutting nippers.

At the Emerald Isle, that hotel's most illustrious and best paying guest roused himself at five o'clock also. At that hour there were no prying chambermaids in the dark corridors to note that, still in his nightshirt, he stole along the hall and rapped discreetly at the doors of two other guests, Messrs. King and Desmond.

Shortly afterward, attired for a dusty drive in the country, he repaired to the dining room for an early breakfast. The sleepy-eyed waitress paid little heed to the fact that two more of the hotel's guests seemed greatly interested also in an early start for whatever might be their activities of the day.

Outside the hotel the streets began to awaken to the usual morning traffic. Clerks arrived at the various mercantile establishments. Shop shutters were opened. Lumber carts rolled ponderously toward the docks and the waiting ships. Riders on horseback went their purposeful ways. It was all quite usual.

John Breslin walked with unhurried steps past the hotel stables, in his hand a small bag. He glanced into the stable yard. Desmond's sorry team already was hitched to the light wagonette he had brought from Perth. A nod from Breslin brought an answering nod from Desmond. The "rich Yankee trader" continued on his way to Albert's stables.

Desmond climbed on the box of his vehicle, glanced back at a large bundle in the body of the wagon, tapped his nags with the whip and wheeled away.

At Albert's livery, King, beside a big, sound-winded black, was talking to a hostler. As Breslin approached, he vaulted into the saddle, chirruped to his horse and rode off.

The door to the stable-yard was open. Breslin walked back to the courtyard, the palms of his hands moist from nervousness. There, to his wonderment, was the matched team he usually hired. Not only were the horses there, but they were harnessed to a light four-wheeled wagonette.

Breslin gave not a thought as to who had hired the rig. Without a moment's hesitation he said: "Ah, you've my wagon ready, I see!"

The half-awake stable hand blinked.

"I'll take it now!" Breslin said, and tossed the hand a half crown.

He swung up to the box, clucked to the team, wheeled them out to the street and tapped them to a trot. It was just half past seven.

Bob Cranston waited until the woebegone sick of the day had disappeared into the doctor's room. He wandered over to the main gate, then straightened his back like the soldier he had been. In his hand he held the forged order. "I have an order for Officer Kooler on the dock, sir," he said, giving the gate guard a military salute.

The guard waved him on with half a glance at the official-looking paper.

Without hurrying, Bob walked to the jetty and up to the Warder Kooler.

"Sir," Bob saluted again, "here is an order from the superintendent."

Kooler peered at it.

"It says——" Bob began.

"I can read," Kooler snapped. "So you got a job for Wilson here and Harrington? Leaves me shorthanded as hell."

"An order, sir," Cranston said in his best military manner.

"All right. Hey, Wilson. You, Harrington. Go with Cranston here."

Straight-faced, Wilson and Harrington fell in behind Cranston. They marched solemnly off the dock and straight for the prison.

And straight past the prison.

Darragh and Hassett looked up as they passed.

"I think old Broomhole can dig his own potatoes," Hassett said.

They walked abreast, Hassett shouldering his spade as he would a rifle.

Hogan saw the little company approach. He filled his brush with a goodly dollop of bright green paint, took careful aim and slapped it with great precision across the front window of Fauntleroy's house. He stepped back to admire his handiwork, picked up his paint pail and joined the procession.

Breslin drove slowly up High Street as if on his way to Perth. Then he reined sharply right and walked his team slowly by the warder's quarters and the main gate of the prison.

The yard of the Establishment was almost deserted, the work details for the day already scattered at their tasks.

Breslin walked his horses on the Rockingham road. Five minutes later wheels rattled behind him. It was Desmond in his wagon. Breslin drove along, Desmond following, until they came to a heavily wooded section of the road. He halted his team, and Desmond came up in back.

In silence they divided the clothing, the guns and ammunition Desmond had brought from Perth. Each took three six-shooters, three caps, three pairs of pants and half the ammunition. They looked to their own pistols and checked the loads.

Both wheeled their teams around. There was not a soul in sight. On both sides of the road the forest of gum, wandoo and jarrah rose in an impenetrable screen. White cockatoos fluttered screaming through the bush. The air was filled with droning insects, in a last frenzy before the cold of winter laid them low. A snake rustled through the dried grass at the edge of the hard macadam road. Bright lizards flashed. Though it was a cool morning, Breslin mopped at the sweat beads on his forehead. Looking at his watch, he nodded silently to Desmond. They tapped their horses and started slowly back toward Fremantle.

It lacked five minutes to eight. Beyond a bend in the dusty Australian road lay success or failure for the months and months of planning.

A minute passed. Two. Three. Then three men in the garb of Her Most Gracious Majesty's prison hove in sight, marching smartly abreast.

Breslin and Desmond whipped their horses to a trot to meet the three: Wilson, Cranston and Harrington. They were grinning from ear to ear. Excitedly, Harrington yelled: "Ireland forever!" Breslin cut him short with a warning hand. "Quiet, for God's sake, quiet!"

The three men jumped into the bed of Desmond's wagon and, before he had a chance to turn back toward Rockingham and whip his horses into a gallop, started to strip off their hated "Broad A" clothes.

The dust cloud back of Desmond's wagon had not settled when three more men came down the road: Darragh, Hassett and Hogan. They ran toward Breslin's wagon, waving their arms and yelling at the top of their voices.

Breslin sawed on the reins and tried to turn his horses around. The three onrushing men startled his mettlesome team. The off-horse reared and pawed the sky. Darragh grabbed at the horse's head. The plunging steed dragged him clear off his feet.

"Let go! He'll kick your head off!" Breslin shouted, forgetting his admonition of only a few minutes before.

Darragh loosed his hold. He fell heavily but scrambled crablike to safety. Breslin slashed at the frantic horse with his whip.

Startled, the animal brought his forefeet down. Breslin lashed him again. Both horses started in an uneven gallop—but a gallop that was taking the wagon back to Fremantle!

Breslin hauled back on the reins and managed to slow the team down. A wide spot in the road gave him the chance he was looking for. He yanked hard and swiveled the horses sharply around, almost upsetting the wagon. The horses headed toward Rockingham. Breslin came abreast of his men and pulled his team to a fast walk. His three passengers jumped aboard. A cut of the whip again and the horses leaped into a punishing gallop.

The men fell on the heap of civilian clothes and started changing. As the wagon rocked along they hurled the prison garb overboard and for the first time in eight years dressed as free men.

They took the tiny hamlet of Ten Mile Well at a sedate walk, though the lathered, heaving horses belied the gait. They had made the ten miles from Fremantle in just forty minutes. Outside the town Breslin drove his team ahead of Desmond's and took the lead.

The going got heavier. Breslin tried to prod the jaded horses to a fast trot. Desmond held just far enough in the rear to escape the clouds of white dust. Some patches of the narrow road were passably hard, others deep sand. Miraculously they had as yet met no other drivers.

They were almost at Rockingham Hotel when Desmond and his passengers heard the drumfire of a horse at furious gallop. He whipped his team up almost to the tailboard of Breslin's wagon. "John! Someone's coming up on horseback!"

Breslin reined his horses back almost on their haunches. "Into the bush!" he shouted.

From both wagons the six Fenians scuttled into the undergrowth like jackrabbits.

The galloping rider clattered around a bend in the road and pulled his horse up short. It was King. He dismounted and knocked the dust off his trousers with his hat. The men popped out of hiding, to meet this partner in the escape and hear his report.

King wiped the sweaty dirt off his face and talked fast. "I rode past the prison a couple of times. There wasn't a sign that anyone had noticed you lads had escaped. Just as I left the town I saw Walsh. He said he'd cut the Bunbury telegraph wires in a dozen places."

"Let's get going," Breslin said. "Fall back a half mile and keep a sharp lookout for any of the English," he ordered King.

Two hours out of Fremantle and ten minutes ahead of schedule, the two dusty wagons wheeled onto the widening in the road that was Rockingham.

The liberated men sat stolidly on the wagon seats, caps pulled down over their eyes, hands on the guns they hid in their pockets.

Breslin waved genially to the proprietor of the Rockingham Hotel, Tom Somers, with whom he had become acquainted on his "Yankee trader" wanderings.

Somers called out: "Hello, Mr. Collins! Just come from Fremantle?"

Breslin nodded.

"Has the *Georgette* sailed yet?" Somers asked.

"She was at the quay when I left," Breslin said.

"She's supposed to be due at the Jarrah jetty this morning. I've mail to go by her," Somers said.

If the *Georgette* made the jetty just as the *Catalpa's* boat was putting to sea, Breslin thought, there might be a fight before they ever saw the whaler. He waved good-by to Somers.

The road petered out in a trail through the sand, which took all the remaining strength out of the horses. In spots all hands but the drivers leaped out and shoved the wheels through dusty pits. The last mile was an agonizing battle at a snail's pace. Precious minutes slid by. Breslin's worries mounted. Sometime before ten-thirty had been the time goal he had set with Anthony. It was nearly that hour as the heavy forest finally gave way to the seaside bush. The goal was near.

On the beach, the bow of the *Catalpa's* whaleboat was pointed seaward. The mast was stayed ready for hoisting sail. The crew lolled in the shade of the sea-edge bush.

Captain Anthony snapped open his big silver watch. It was nearly ten-thirty. If Breslin had got his men out of Fremantle at eight o'clock, then they should be here within the next ten minutes. He strained his ears for the noise of horses breaking through the bush—or the revolver shots that would mean a running battle with the police. All he heard was the noise of the surf, the sighing of the wind in the gum trees, the screams of the feeding gulls.

The keen ears of Gingy, the Malay deckhand, caught the sound first. He jumped to his feet. "Cap'n!" he cried. "Wagon come! Horses come! I hear!"

Suddenly Breslin's team burst through the bush in a flurry of sand. Close behind him came Desmond. Out of the two wagons piled the bronzed, bearded escapees, waving their revolvers.

"Him pirates!" Mopsy screamed.

"No pirates, all friends," Captain Anthony shouted.

King and the six Fenians rushed for the boat, grabbed the gunwales and began to drag it to the water's edge.

"Him steal boat!" Gingy wrung his hands.

Breslin and Desmond yanked their steaming teams around in the sand, leaped from the drivers' seats and slashed the frantic horses across their rumps. The frenzied nags dashed blindly back into the sandy trace from which they had just burst and tangled traces inextricably with the underbrush. Snarled like that, they would effectually block off pursuers. Breslin gave King's jaded horse a belt on the flanks and sent him snorting into the mass of harness and flailing hooves. Then he raced to Captain Anthony.

"We did it, Captain! We did it!" he cried. "They all got clean away—the whole lot of 'em. Hère they are, all free men at last!"

Anthony pounded him on the back. "There's not a minute to waste. The bark's offshore, ready and waiting for us!" He started for the boat. The *Catalpa* men stood stiff with fear. Under the direction of King and Desmond the Fenians were trying to launch the craft.

"Get the hell away from that boat!" Anthony yelled. "You'll swamp it! Let my men handle it!"

The *Catalpa* boat crew jerked into action.

From the nearby jetty Ball came running. "What's going on here?" he demanded. "Do you need help, Captain? What are you doing to those horses?"

"In the boat! Everybody!" Anthony yelled.

Breslin shoved a sovereign into Ball's hand. "The horses can go to hell!" he cried excitedly. "You drive them there!"

The loaded boat wallowed in the surf. Breslin splashed through the white water and hurled himself aboard.

Ball stood open-mouthed, the sovereign clutched in his hand.

Captain Anthony grabbed the big steering oar.

"You passengers! Down! Down in the bottom of the boat! Give us room to row!" he shouted.

Breslin, King, Desmond and the six threw themselves in the bottom of the whaleboat, trying desperately to keep clear of the feet of the oarsmen.

"Pull!" the Captain yelled. "Pull!"

The thirty-foot-long overloaded boat scarcely stirred to the first ill-timed strokes. Waves lapped her gunwales. She began to drift broadside of the surf. Water swept overside. She rolled loglike under the weight of sixteen men and her gear.

"*Pull!*" the captain shouted again. "Pull like you were pulling for a whale! *Pull!* Big Louie, come on! Give 'em stroke! Pull you, Toby. Down on it, Mopsy. Pull . . . pull . . . *pull!* Down together! That's the stuff!"

The great oars finally bit in unison. A white wake trailed aft.

Despite the confusion, scarcely three minutes had elapsed from the time the rescued and rescuers had broken through the bush until the *Catalpa's* boat was driving steadily out to sea.

Ashore Ball broke into a run for the timber jetty. Breslin watched through the captain's telescope. He saw Ball mount a horse and whip him into a gallop.

At half after eleven, an hour from the time she had left the beach, the whaleboat was two miles offshore.

Breslin kept the telescope trained on shore.

Suddenly he stiffened. "The police!" he said.

Where the whaleboat had been launched, a knot of uniformed men had gathered. Some pointed toward the boat. Others worked to untangle the snarled teams. Soon all the men mounted and disappeared in the sand trace leading through the bush.

The excitement in Breslin's flashing eyes and in his vibrant voice was contagious. Even the still bewildered crewmen joined timidly in the three cheers he demanded for "The bravest captain of them all—Captain George Anthony! Hip . . . hip . . . hurrah!"

As the cheers subsided, he said triumphantly: "Tis done, Captain. Now all I have to do is to inform His Excellency, the Governor of West Australia, as to just what has transpired."

He reached into his coat pocket and fished out a folded bit of oilskin. Unwrapping it, he withdrew a sheet of paper. He held it up and, in a voice that choked with emotion, proudly read:

"To His Excellency,
The British Governor of West Australia:
This is to certify that I have this day released from the clemency of Her Most Gracious Majesty, Victoria, Queen of Great Britain, etc., etc., etc., six Irishmen, condemned to imprisonment for life by the enlightened and magnanimous government of Great Britain for having been guilty of the atrocious and unpardonable crimes known to the unenlightened portion of mankind as 'Love of Liberty' and 'Hatred of Tyranny.' For this act of 'Irish Assurance' my birth and my blood being my full and sufficient warrant. Allow me to add that:

> I'm taking my leave now, I've only to say
> A few cells I've emptied (a sell in its way).
> I've the honor and pleasure to bid you good-day.
> From all future acquaintance, excuse me, I pray.
In the service of my country,

John J. Breslin."

Breslin flourished the paper dramatically before the bewildered eyes of the oarsmen, folded it carefully, wrapped it in its oilskin, then tied the packet with a bit of spun yarn. Taking a hatchet he hacked off a piece of one of the thwarts and bound the packet to it. Then he took a red waif flag and set it in a cleft in the bit of board to act as a sail.

The whaleboat was still well inside Garden Island with the wind and tide setting full ashore. Breslin launched his tiny craft and watched it as it danced shoreward. Grinning, he blew a kiss to the little sailboat.

"Now, Captain Anthony," he said. "Let's for the *Catalpa* and America!"

15 . The Catalpa Stands to Sea

Two flies butted their heads stubbornly against the sun-flooded windows in Prison Superintendent Donan's austere office. Mr. Donan eyed them critically as he reached for the sheaf of documents that required his official attention this April morning. Just like the fools penned up here, he mused. Down-under winter coming on, a frosty chill in the morning air, yet all they could think of was getting out.

He checked the big wall clock against his heavy gold watch— 10:45 A.M. Resignedly he turned to the papers before him. Atop the pile was the list of punishments to be meted out next day.

He came to the bottom of the pile. "Approved!" he barked to a waiting orderly. "Summon Mr. Atcheson and Mr. Ferguson!"

He drummed on the desk as he awaited the appearance of the two prison officials. His thoughts drifted momentarily to the pleasures that lay ahead this day. There was a fresh uniform waiting for him at home. Thus attired he would mingle elegantly with the guests of honor and even His Excellency, the Governor himself, at the laying of the cornerstone for the new Freemason's building this very afternoon.

Atcheson and Ferguson arrived. They bowed obsequiously and took the chairs indicated by Donan. Scarcely had they been seated than, from without, a bull-like voice bellowed. The door of the office burst open.

Donan leaped to his feet, his face crimson. "Mister Fauntleroy!" he roared. "What is the meaning of this intrusion? When I wish to speak with you or any other of my officials, I'll send for you!"

Mr. Fauntleroy shook a bony finger accusingly at his chief. "Where is he?" he shrieked. "Where is the despoiler of my 'ouse? Where is that traitorous Irishman? I demand five hundred lashes on his back. I demand solitary for six months for the fiend. My 'ouse! My 'ouse!"

Donan's hand stemmed the tirade. "What are you screaming about? What's this about your house?"

"He was painting it. Your blasted convict Hogan was painting it! He ruined it! He's sloshed green paint right across my parlor windows! I want justice!"

Donan turned to Atcheson. "Fetch Hogan here at once," he ordered.

The warden started for the door, but before he could reach it, another man stomped angrily into the office. "You, Atcheson!" he shouted. "What do you mean taking away the men who were planting my potatoes? If they ain't planted now, I won't have none. What kind of a prison are we running here anyhow?"

Donan looked helplessly at Atcheson.

"Now what?" he asked.

"That would be Hassett and Darragh, sir!"

"Did you order them to cease work at Mr. Broomhole's place?"

"No, sir. Not me. Their orders was to plant them potatoes and stay on the job until they was planted complete."

"Planted complete?" Broomhole shouted. "Two holes they dug, then took off."

Donan's face turned a deep purple. "I'll teach those damned Irishmen a lesson! You, Ferguson! You, Atcheson! Get them!"

The warders scurried off. Thirty minutes went by. Donan paced angrily. Atcheson ducked into the room. Donan whirled on him: "Well?"

Atcheson cringed. "We ain't found them yet!"

"A plot!" Donan screeched. "Sound the alarm bell! Recall all work parties! Muster all prisoners!"

The clanging of the great bell hushed the streets of Fremantle. Townsfolk looked at each other in surprise. Only a disaster at the Establishment called for a general alarm.

In the cool shadows of his church, Father McCabe heard the bell's brazen voice. He looked at his watch. It lacked a few minutes of noon. If all was going well, the Fenians were safe in the *Catalpa*'s boat. He smiled, then dropped to his knees in prayer.

The convict population of the Establishment was lined up on the parade. Names were ticked off on the rolls. Six failed to answer call.

"A plot!" Donan roared. "A damned traitor Irish plot! Get me trackers. Get on their trail. I want those six men in chains before nightfall!"

He wheeled on Atcheson, who trembled beside him. "This is a matter for the highest authorities! Get to the telegraph office! Wire the constabulary at Perth! Alert them that six of our most dangerous criminals have absconded! Run!"

Ferguson dashed for the telegraph office on the waterfront a half dozen blocks away. He found the operator twiddling his thumbs. "Something's wrong with the wires," the man said. "Can't get through to Perth nor to Bunbury neither. We're trying to find out what's wrong."

Ferguson stepped out on the street only to duck back as fast as he could leap, as a horse thundered past the telegraph office at a mad gallop. Its rider was shouting at the top of his lungs: "Help! Pirates! Pirates! Police!"

The horseman pulled his steed back on its haunches as he came abreast of the office of the Water Police. It was Ball, the only witness to the dramatic happenings at the beach at Rockingham. He had made the twenty miles in the almost incredible time of one hour and forty minutes.

The Water Police office was quickly jammed with townsfolk, all clamoring to hear Ball's story. In the midst of the confusion Water Police Superintendent Stone arrived in the elegant equipage he had hired from Albert's livery for his visit to his ailing relative in Perth. Stone, a tall, angular, powerful man with a close-cropped mustache and bristling iron-gray hair, shoved his way through the crowd. Ferguson followed hard on his heels.

"What's all this now?" Stone demanded. "Constables, clear out some of these people. Let's have order! Now, sir, what's this about pirates?"

Ball blurted out his story.

Stone began questioning him. "How many men were there?"

"Nine."

"Describe them!"

"Well, the one that was the leader was big and had a full beard. He was well dressed. Two others was well got up too. They all had hats. Then there was six others . . ."

Ferguson pricked up his ears.

"They had on bad-fitting clothes and caps."

"Armed?"

"All of 'em had revolvers or pistols."

Ferguson asked: "Captain Stone, may I question Mr. Ball, please?"

Stone nodded.

"Did you see any of those six close enough to tell what they looked like?" Ferguson asked.

"Well . . . One was terrible dark, almost like a blackfellow. One had real red hair . . . Another had a big scar on his face."

Ferguson gave a triumphant shout. "Them's our men!"

"What do you mean?" Stone asked.

"I mean, sir, that six of our most dangerous criminals—the notorious Irish Fenian traitors—absconded this morning. The men Ball describes are those escaped Irishmen. Superintendent Donan must hear of this at once!" Ferguson shoved through the crowd and legged it for the prison. In fifteen minutes he was back with a puffing Donan.

"Where are those dastards?" Donan screeched. "I'll hang them! So help me, I'll hang them all!"

Stone calmed him. "First we'll have to get at the bottom of what looks like a clever plot hatched under our very noses. Then we'll have to catch them. Then we'll talk about hanging them."

Governor Robinson arrived in Fremantle at two o'clock that afternoon, prepared to be the honor guest at the Masonic festivities, but instead was thrust immediately into the maelstrom of investigation. Stone and Donan had arrived at a pretty shrewd conclusion as to just what had happened. The slashes in the telegraph lines had been found and repairs made. Townsfolk quickly identified Ball's bearded man as the "Yankee trader" Collins. The Fremantle telegraph operator dug up copies of the communications that had passed between Collins and the American whaling captain Anthony. The ship was identified as the *Catalpa,* out of New Bedford.

"Good detective work, men," Governor Robinson praised. "Now what has been done to apprehend these desperadoes?"

Stone spoke up. "I have dispatched our Water Police cutter, under command of Coxswain Mills—a brave, capable man—with a crew of ten, to search the waters off Rottnest and Garden Island. Mills has orders to intercept the whaleboat, arrest everyone in it and bring them to port here."

"And, by the Eternal, I'll have ropes ready to hang them all—convicts and Yankees alike!" Donan roared.

"First we must catch them!" Governor Robinson said drily. "Then there is such a thing as international law."

"International law be hanged!" Donan said. "The law here is the law we make. I'll see that the law calls for a noose!"

Governor Robinson shook his head. "This is evidently a well-thought-out plot. It is too bad the *Conflict* has departed. We could use her speed and her guns. I shall dispatch messages immediately to all ports where she is to call, instructing her captain to turn back for Fremantle at full speed."

"She'll arrive too late!" Donan said dourly.

"I fear that. If there only was another fast . . ."

"The *Georgette* is still at dock. I don't think she's coaled yet!" Atcheson offered.

"Capital!" Governor Robinson beamed. "Mr. Stone, I commission the *Georgette* forthwith as a warship in Her Majesty's Navy. You will be in complete command. Her Captain—what is his name?"

"Grady, sir."

"Captain Grady, then, will take orders from you, Mr. Stone. What armed forces are available locally?"

"We have a well-drilled company of the Enlisted Pensioners' Reserve, your Excellency."

"Muster them at once. Notify the *Georgette*'s agent and her Captain. Now I must make an appearance at the Masonic ceremonies, but I shall be back shortly. Have the *Georgette*'s Captain here when I return."

The Governor was back at Stone's office by 4:30 P.M. Captain Grady of the *Georgette* was waiting impatiently. Stone's face was flushed.

"Ah, Captain Grady!" the Governor said. "No doubt Mr. Stone has acquainted you with the facts in the case."

"He has," Grady replied gruffly. "And he has also informed me that he is in command of my ship!"

"I have put Mr. Stone in complete charge of this action, Captain. You are correctly informed."

"Then I protest, sir, here and now. The *Georgette* is my command. I am responsible to her owners. I protest, sir."

"I quite appreciate your feelings . . ."

"I don't think you do, your Excellency. Besides, Mr. Stone is already demanding the impossible. He wants to sail at once. My crew is tired . . ."

"Tired because they caroused all the Easter weekend!" Stone said.

"I resent that, sir!" Captain Grady flashed. "Besides, my ship is not coaled. I cannot undertake a long voyage——"

"Is a voyage to Rottnest Island such an ocean adventure?" Stone asked sarcastically.

"Gentlemen! We'll have no more of this bickering!" the Governor interrupted. "My orders stand. You will work together in this expedition. Remember, gentlemen, this is a duty to our country and our Queen!"

"The Queen!" Stone and Grady chorused.

The office door opened. Coxswain Mills strode in. He saluted Stone.

"What brings you back so soon, Mr. Mills?" Stone demanded.

Mills took an oilskin-wrapped packet from his coat pocket. "I spoke a coastwise schooner shortly after leaving," he reported. "Her skipper picked up this packet, tied to a bit of board, with a waif flag for sail. I took the liberty of opening it and deemed the message of such importance that I decided to deliver it to you at once."

Stone opened the packet.

"It is a letter addressed to your Excellency!" He handed it to Governor Robinson.

The Governor read the message carefully, first to himself, then aloud.

"John J. Breslin," he repeated. "It sounds familiar but . . ."

A Water Police constable spoke up. "If it please your Excellency . . ."

"Yes, my man?"

"My name is Mulcahy. I'm amnestied. I was in prison . . . years ago. You understand . . ."

"Yes! Yes! You know this Breslin?"

"That I do, sir. He liberated James Stephens from Dublin prison back in the '60's, sir, beggin' your pardon for offering my word to you."

"Ha!" Governor Robinson slapped his thigh. "That's it. Now I remember. Breslin was a master conspirator. What a coup if we can catch him! Mr. Stone, now we know the caliber of our enemy. He has plotted carefully. He is cunning. It will take our most valiant efforts to thwart him. Is your armed force on the *Georgette*?"

"Within the hour, sir! The Pensioners are in charge of Major Flaherty. The Water Police detail is in charge of Sergeant Mc-Larty."

"Flaherty! McLarty! Have we none but Irishmen hereabouts? Are you sure you can trust such men?"

Stone stiffened. "Sir," he said with some hauteur, "they are my most trusted officers. I can answer personally as to their loyalties to Her Majesty. They will bring back the criminals."

"I do not doubt it. Now, your orders. I will draft them and sign the document directly, but I will give them to you verbally at once. You are to pursue these fugitives, if they are still in the whaleboat, or, if they are aboard the whaler, you are hereby directed to identify the ship, to go alongside her, to demand the surrender of the criminals being harbored thereon. You will warn the Captain, with as much show of force as you may deem necessary, of the consequences of his rash deed in defying the forces of Her Majesty!"

"Thank you, sir! I shall do my utmost."

"England asks nothing more!"

Stone turned to Mills. "Coxswain, refresh your men, set sail as soon as possible. You heard the Governor's orders. Obey them. How are the winds?"

"Light and westerly, sir."

Stone rubbed his hands in satisfaction. "A lumbering whaler can make little westerly progress under such conditions. If the winds do not pick up, I am confident, Governor Robinson, that our quarry will not be too far away by tomorrow morning. She must depend on the wind. The *Georgette* has sails—and she has her engine."

Before Governor Robinson left for Perth Monday night, he drafted this message for immediate telegraphic transmission to all points in the Commonwealth:

"Detain, by force if necessary, American whaling bark *Catalpa*, George Anthony master. Arrest said Anthony, his officers and crew and any passengers who may be aboard. These passengers are believed to be six life-term convicts who have this day absconded from Her Majesty's penal establishment in Fremantle. Immediately upon seizure of ship and men, notify proper authorities in Fremantle and Perth."

Telegraph sounders clicked in Adelaide, in Melbourne, in Sydney, Brisbane, Darwin—and in Bunbury.

Bea Warren took the message.

So that was why that Sam Smith never showed up at the picnic. He was just a criminal. Why, he was like a traitor! Maybe they'd

196

hang him. She sobered at the thought. Maybe, though, since he was a Yank, they'd just put him in jail for years and years. Maybe she'd see Mr. Sam Smith again—on visitor's day at the Establishment. It would be worth the long stagecoach trip—and she'd wear the gold brooch too!

Sam Smith was a lonely mariner on a lonely sea. If his thoughts wandered at all that Monday, they most certainly did not trend toward Bea Warren. More likely they raced the thousands of miles of ocean to a tidy spot in Martha's Vineyard, and to pretty Amy Chase Jernegan there. And when he thought of Amy Chase, his heart was heavy as a sounding lead. For the outlook was dim that he would see her fresh young face for many and many a day—if he ever did see her again.

For Sam had made a great decision while he watched his Captain's boat merge into the shore haze on Sunday evening. If George came back safely, with or without the Irishmen, all well and good. If the English came after them, then he'd go down with the ship, fighting beside his friend and captain with revolver, musket, lance and cutting spade to the end.

But if George didn't come back, if he was caught by the English and thrown into prison, then he, Sam Smith, would be eternally damned if he would turn stern and run for New Bedford—whether that was orders or not. He would head straight for Fremantle harbor and get George Anthony out of prison if he had to shoot his way in and fight his way out. If he didn't do that, then he knew he could never face Amy Chase or Emmie Anthony again.

But there was little time for planning so far ahead. Sam's immediate job was to work the *Catalpa* far enough offshore so that she would be in international waters and thus outside the legal jurisdiction of Australian authorities. Not that Sam had any faith whatever in international law. If the English wanted their men, and their men were on the *Catalpa*, well—it was a far piece to America and it would be a long time before Washington ever heard of any violation of sea law.

The winds were contrarily light all Sunday night. By daylight

Monday the bark had made scarcely a mile more in her westward course. The sails had hung limply until near sun-up, when a light breeze from the west sprung up.

Sam drove his crew mercilessly, trying every sailing trick he knew to win a few more miles offshore. Anthony had told him twelve miles would be enough, but Sam took it on himself to add four miles more to that—a good sixteen miles of open water to give them plenty of room to outsmart the British. By taking advantage of every little cat's-paw of wind he reached his goal by noontime Monday. All canvas except a headsail and the fore and main topsails were clewed, and the *Catalpa* began her slow patrol of the Australian coast, waiting for the return of her Captain.

The afternoon wore along. Relief followed relief at the lookout rings. There was no sign of the whaleboat.

Around four in the afternoon the wind picked up and the sky clouded over. Whitecaps dotted the water, making it more and more difficult for the men aloft to spot the small boat. The *Catalpa* began to roll and pitch.

Darkness closed in. Sam climbed to the mainmast rings with his spyglass for a last futile look. If Captain Anthony had taken the men off the beach at half after ten, as he had planned, then he should have been this far offshore hours ago. Maybe . . . But Sam shut the ugly thought of capture out of his mind.

"Mr. Boles," he called, "keep a man in each ring for the rest of the night. I want lanterns lashed at the topgallant doublings in the foremast, mainmast and mizzen. I want her riding lights bright and shining. And put another lantern at her bow. I want her to look like a floating city, so even if we can't spot him, the Captain can find us in the dark."

At four in the afternoon, Captain Anthony pointed the overloaded boat more into the wind. It was slow going with the breeze still from the west, but by good seamanship the whaleboat began to win an appreciable distance from shore. But there was not a sail in sight, only the dipping terns, the dancing water, the shimmering western horizon where the sun was getting low.

Captain Anthony leaned toward Breslin. In a low whisper he said: "If we don't raise the bark soon, we'll have to spend the night in the boat."

"What are our chances?" Breslin asked anxiously.

Suddenly Second Mate Farnham, in the bow, balanced himself against the clumsy cleat for another searching look. The whaleboat crested a sea as he peered ahead. He waited for another sea to raise the boat. Then he said, simply: "There ship."

By five o'clock any one of them could see the bark's upper courses when the whaleboat was atop the crest of a sea. The *Catalpa* was holding a course roughly parallel with the shore and was about eight miles away from them. The whaleboat was gaining on her but slowly. There was no indication from the bark that her lookouts had sighted them.

With an awe-inspiring rush, great banks of ominous black clouds suddenly blotted out the setting sun and the whole western sky. The wind shipped up sharply. A rain squall laid a curtain about the bark, cutting it from view, doused the already soaked men in the whaleboat, and churned the sea into froth.

The sail strained in the gusts and the boat picked up speed.

"In oars!" Captain Anthony ordered, and took a fresh grip on the steering sweep.

Another knockdown squall heeled the whaleboat so her lee gunwale shipped water.

"You! You!" Anthony pointed at Hogan and Cranston. "Grab the scoops and bail! The rest of you, up on the weather rail—the one most out of the water! Quick, afore the next squall hits!"

Despite the balancing weight, the boat shipped another wave. Water was inches deep in the bottom. Hogan and Cranston bailed frantically. Wave after wave sent more water over the side and threatened to swamp the overloaded craft.

It was pitch dark. There was no longer hope of fighting their way to the *Catalpa*. It was a question now of survival.

With a rush and a roar another savage squall hit.

Panic gripped the Irishmen, none of whom had ever had experience in rough water in a small boat. Hogan dropped his bailing scoop with a splash to the bottom. "I'll drown!" he cried. "I'll drown! Holy Mother of God, save me . . ."

"Don't be so damn selfish," Darragh said grimly. "Ask for help for the rest of us!"

"Shut up," Breslin snapped. "We're all in the same boat, and we'll sink or swim together. Now bail!"

Hogan grabbed his scoop and bailed furiously.

Darragh began to sing, so softly at first the wind carried his words away. Then his voice gained strength:

"Jesus, Lover of my soul,
　Let me to Thy bosom fly.
While the nearer waters roll,
　While the tempest still is high;
Hide me, O my Saviour, hide,
　Till the storm of life is past;
Safe into the haven guide;
　O, receive my soul at last!"

Hogan wiped his eyes with salty hands, then blindly resumed his bailing.

Wilson clapped Darragh on the back. "Well done! But let's give these *Catalpa* boys something to cheer 'em. Give 'em 'The Rising of the Moon!' "

The *Catalpa* men grinned as the Irishmen shouted the words into the teeth of the wind:

"Death to every foe and traitor.
　Forward, strike the marching tune
And hurrah, me boys, for Freedom!
　'Tis the Rising of the Moon!"

As they finished the song, another rain squall lashed the sea to whitecapped fury and threatened to shred the sail or break the mast. At a little past seven o'clock, the worst squall of all raced down on them with the roar of an express train and a torrent of rain. Captain Anthony heaved on the steering oar, trying to pay

200

off the boat and spill wind out of the sail, but his efforts were in vain. The mast snapped short at the step. Mast, mainsail, jib, halyards, rigging—all collapsed overside in a snarled mess. The boat started to swing broadside.

The Captain battled to keep the near-foundering craft into the wind. Luckily the mass in the water acted like a sea anchor and aided him. White water cascaded into the boat.

Second Mate Farnham grabbed a hatchet and hacked away at the ropes. By brute strength he and a seaman dragged the mess inboard.

In the belly of the boat all the passengers bailed for their lives with scoops, caps, bare hands.

Desperately the *Catalpa* men dug their oars into the seas, forcing the boat into the wind so repairs could be made.

It was ten o'clock before Farnham had a jury mast rigged and a rag of sail set.

The Captain gave the men a respite from the oars as he let the sail fill, then spilled it when the gusts came too strong. With aching muscles and bleeding palms he still clung grimly to the steering oar.

Unless they could spot the lights of the *Catalpa,* there was no chance of their reaching the ship before daybreak. A lighted lantern would serve only to make the whaleboat easy prey for the English. The provisions were ruined. The ham had been swept overboard. The biscuits were a salty mush. There was some water left, and in the boat's emergency kegs, put there months before, were dry biscuits. There was rum enough for a swig all around. He passed the bottle around. Stolidly each took his swallow. Farnham doled out the biscuits and a gill of water to wash them down. The next meal they would get would be aboard the *Catalpa*—or in an English prison.

Silently they worried through the night, cold, wet, fearful. Toward dawn the wind moderated appreciably and the squalls ceased entirely. Daybreak brought a blood-red sun that glinted through ragged clouds on heavy seas.

The whaleboat actually had made a good mile more seaward in her battle with the squalls. The land was dim gray about four miles distant. But there was no sign of the *Catalpa*.

Wearily the crew took to the oars again. With the wind more northerly, the boat made good progress seaward.

At about a quarter to seven, Tuesday morning, Mate Farnham once more spotted the *Catalpa*. "She's a-headin' right for us!" he cried jubilantly.

"We'll fetch her for sure now, Mr. Breslin!" Captain Anthony pledged.

Breslin nodded, then turned his eyes astern. "Give me your glass," he said suddenly. "Look! Is that smoke on the horizon?"

Captain Anthony studied the sea through the telescope. Finally he said: "It's a steamer with engine going and all sails set too. There's only one ship hereabouts with sails and steam. She's the *Georgette*!"

They alternated with the glass. Anthony shook his head. "She can't have raised us at that distance. She's headed for the *Catalpa*. We'd better make ourselves scarce as we can, just in case some fool British lookout looks our way instead of at the ship." He barked to Farnham: "Mr. Farnham, yank that sail down. Drop the mast. You men, in oars. All of you, down on the bottom. That goes for you too, Mr. Breslin. I'll crouch low, seeing I've got to hang onto this sweep."

The *Georgette* steamed rapidly toward them, her funnel pouring black smoke, her paddle-wheels churning a white wake.

She came within five miles of them on a course set directly for the *Catalpa*. Evidently the men in her masthead lookouts had eyes only for the whaler.

"I hope Sam's got a good story ready," Captain Anthony muttered to Breslin. "He's likely to need it right soon."

First Mate Smith was weary after the stormy night. He had had a few minutes sleep after the worst of the squalls had ceased, but before dawn he was on deck, spyglass in hand, waiting for enough daylight to look for the Captain and the whaleboat. Look-outs were posted long before the red sun cracked the eastern sky.

There was no sign of the boat. What the wild weather of the night just over might have done to her . . . Well, if anyone could have kept an overloaded boat afloat, it was George.

At eight o'clock the foremast lookout shouted: "Sail ho!"

Smith leaped for the maintop. "I see her." His hopes fell. "Steamer, ain't she?"

"She smoke, sar. Sails too."

That would be the government ship, the *Georgette*. One sure thing, she wasn't carrying the mails this trip.

On deck, he gave swift orders. "Mr. Bolles, get out a couple muskets. Have some right sharp spades and lances ready. Mebbe we'll be needin' 'em!"

In about two hours the *Georgette* chuffed alongside. Her paddle-wheels were slowed down and she carried on by her sails.

Though Sam could not know it, she was manned by a crew surly because their stay in Fremantle had been cut short, and captained by a master who openly resented the high-handed action of the Governor in giving full command of his ship to Water Police Superintendent Stone. Captain Grady was barely civil to Stone, though, as instructed by Governor Robinson, he punctiliously obeyed every order. And an order came now.

"Bring me up to speaking distance, Mr. Grady," Stone said.

The two ships lolled along side by side.

Smith studiously kept his eyes averted from the Englishman.

Stone put trumpet to lips. "What ship is that?" he bellowed.

Sam turned languidly, sauntered to the rail of the *Catalpa* and lazily put his own trumpet to use. "Bark *Catalpa*, outa New Bedford, Massachusetts, United States of America. If you'd looked at her fantail you could ha' read it yourself!" he replied in the broadest Yankee drawl he could produce. "Who in hell be ye?"

"This is Her Majesty's ship of war *Georgette*!" Stone began.

"Hell of a lookin' warship," Sam jibed. "Whar's yer guns?"

"Never mind our guns," Stone said. "What is your business?"

"Business is mindin' my own business," Sam retorted. "What's yours?"

"You'll find out mighty soon. I repeat, what's your business?"

"I'm on th' high seas, as any fool can see," Sam countered.

"I insist on knowing your business."

"We're whalin' if you must know."

"Your larboard boat is missing."

Sam looked at the empty davits. "So 'tis, so 'tis," he said.

"Where is it?"

Sam hesitated. "Captain has it."

"Who is he?"

"Captain Anthony."

Stone smiled in satisfaction. "Where is he?"

"Gone to Fremantle to buy us an anchor."

"Why didn't you sail there?"

"That's th' Captain's business."

"Have you seen anything of a whaleboat with many men in it?" Stone shouted. "We're looking for prisoners who escaped from Her Majesty's prison in Fremantle."

Sam grinned from ear to ear. "Hain't sighted another craft all mornin' 'cept you."

"I am going to board your ship!" Stone declared.

The ships were a hundred yards apart.

Sam dropped his trumpet to the deck. "Like hell you are!" he roared.

"I'm going to board you and search for prisoners!"

"You try it an' you'll be goddam good and sorry! I'm on the high seas, outside your waters! You got no right to board me! What the hell did we lick the pants offn' you damn Britishers in 1812 about? You don't own the ocean!"

Stone ignored the jibe. "I'm coming aboard!" he shouted.

Sam boiled. His face was turkey-red. "By God, you ain't! You'll git yourself in bad trouble! And you'll git me in trouble too. I'm responsible for this here ship when th' Captain's off her. You stay clear!"

"Bring me alongside!" Stone yelled to Captain Grady.

The *Georgette's* master shrugged. He gave the order to his helmsman and signaled the engine room. The government ship, twice the size of the whaler, closed slowly in.

"Take your stinkin' coal scow off! You're smudgin' my canvas!" Sam pointed dramatically to the already dingy, oil-greasy sails on the bark. "Shear off, goddam you! Sheer off!" He grabbed a razor-sharp lance, drew it back and poised it in his sinewy hand as if he were going to kill a whale.

Stone held a hurried conference with the senior officer of the Reservists and of his own police detail.

Captain Grady eyed the gesticulating huddle with contempt. All this pother over a parcel of political prisoners. England would be better off with their hungry mouths outside prison walls. Let them all escape. What difference would it make to the governor, the prime minister—or the Queen herself?

Then a grease-daubed chief engineer emerged from the engine room. He saluted and whispered agitatedly to the Captain. Grady nodded and smiled in smug self-satisfaction, as he swaggered over to Stone. "A word with you, Mr. Stone!" he said. "If you are done conferring, and don't want to row back to Fremantle, I'd suggest you give me orders to steam back immediatly. My engineer warns me we have barely enough coal in our bunkers to take us there!"

"But I thought you were coaled . . ." Stone spluttered.

"Coaled, hell! We hadn't even got a pound aboard when you ordered us out last night."

Stone bowed to the inevitable. "All right," he said. "You may set course for Fremantle."

The *Georgette* sheared away from the *Catalpa.*

A puzzled Sam watched her every move. Well, he'd won that round. Now to raise Captain Anthony.

A frustrated Water Police chief, a disappointed, half-seasick company of Pensioners, a smug captain and a sullen crew watched the *Catalpa* fade into the distance. Captain Grady ordered his lookouts alow, keeping only one man in the bow as a gesture to the search for the whaleboat.

Off Cape Bouvard, the *Georgette* spoke the Water Police cutter, under Coxswain Mills, bowling along. Stone hailed it.

"Coxswain," he yelled, "we found the bark, but the prisoners have not yet reached it. They must still be in the whaler's small boat. Keep a keen eye out for it. It should be somewhere off Murray Head, by my reckoning."

From about four miles away Captain Anthony and Breslin watched every movement of the two ships.

They could imagine what was going on. The shortness of the close encounter before the *Georgette* bore away indicated the English were satisfied there were no escaped men aboard the bark. The *Georgette's* northerly course after leaving the bark would take her directly to Fremantle. The only strange maneuver was the *Catalpa's* setting off on a course that was south-southeast, directly away from the area where Smith should have kept his rendezvous with the whaleboat.

Captain Anthony studied the *Georgette* through his glass. Suddenly he said, "Mr. Breslin, that Britisher hasn't got a lookout posted aloft."

Out came the oars. The *Georgette* was about eight miles away, still on her northerly course. The *Catalpa* was about twelve miles to the south, still on her southeasterly course.

Then Breslin warned the Captain the *Georgette* had changed her course and now, while still heading toward Fremantle, seemed to be continuing her search for them along shore. If she stayed on the new tack and stood out to sea only a short distance, they would be directly in her path. If that happened, only blind men could fail to spot them.

The *Catalpa* was hull down on the horizon.

"She's a ghost ship," Wilson muttered despairingly as he and the rescued men huddled disconsolately on the bottom of the boat.

The *Georgette* bore toward them. Once more Anthony ordered

all down in the wet bottom. The whaleboat drifted like a weary log on the heaving sea.

About one o'clock in the afternoon the *Georgette* steamed across their stern so closely that, even without the spyglass, Anthony and Breslin could make out the men on her deck. Thanks to the decision of Captain Grady, they went unnoticed. The steamer rolled right on, her plume of black smoke settling in her milky wake. As soon as she was nearly hull down, Captain Anthony ordered the oars out again. Wearily the men rowed after the vanishing *Catalpa*, now scarcely visible on the far horizon ahead.

Second Mate Farnham balanced himself by the mast and watched the ship. "Bark's on new tack!" he announced suddenly.

The *Catalpa* began to loom larger and larger. Perhaps she had sighted them after all and had stood away to befuddle the *Georgette*'s master. At any rate, she was heading directly for them.

Breslin grabbed a red waif flag, and thrust it into Wilson's hands. "Get up in the bow," he ordered. "Wave like hell."

The bark broke out all but her topgallant sails and headed down on them. Sam Smith must have spotted them. It was half past two.

The set, grim faces of the men in the whaleboat gave way to grins of delight. It was all over now. In a few minutes they would be safe aboard. But in the distance another vessel under full sail was racing for the bark.

"She's the Water Police cutter," Breslin said gloomily after a study through the glass.

The cutter was booming along about as far distant on the landward side of the *Catalpa* as the whaleboat was to seaward.

"Dig in! Dig in!" Captain Anthony yelled to his crew.

There wasn't any need for his exhortations. Every man knew by now he had helped English Crown prisoners escape jail. Every one of the *Catalpa* men knew that capture meant weeks, months, maybe years in the very prison from which their passengers had fled.

The six rescued men, King and Desmond huddled in the bottom, trying desperately to keep out of the way of the straining legs and the muscular arms of the oarsmen. Breslin sat stiffly beside the Captain, fingering his rosary.

In the freshening late afternoon wind, the cutter was forced to luff frequently, to spill the wind from her overburdened mainsail. Each time the cutter luffed, the whaleboat gained a tiny advantage.

White water curled from the slim bow of the police boat. The heavily laden whaleboat lumbered on desperately. The *Catalpa* pounded majestically toward both. The cutter still was a hundred yards away from the *Catalpa* when the whaleboat swept alongside the bark.

First Mate Smith and his crew were ready. As the whaleboat slammed alongside he yelled: "Hard aback!" The great yards were braced about to cut the bark's forward motion. He threw the forward boat tackle to Farnham and the aft tackle to Anthony. Both made fast.

"Grab those grip lines, you passengers!" Anthony yelled. "Get aboard the bark."

Like monkeys the Irishmen clambered over the *Catalpa*'s rail, the whaleboat crew hard on their heels. Anthony was last aboard. The cutter was only a scant hundred feet away.

"Show him our weapons!" Captain Anthony shouted.

Sam and Bolles aimed their muskets. The lance blades glittered.

The coxswain of the cutter looked at the arms he faced, then eyed his ten-man detail. Hell, the Governor hadn't said anything about getting killed in this hunt. Like as not someone would get hurt boarding against such odds. This was a job for a big force. Superintendent Stone himself could come out and get these men. He luffed the cutter.

"He's licked!" Captain Anthony pounded Sam on the back.

The *Catalpa* wore ship. In two minutes she was on her new course and the cutter was dropping behind.

In the twilight the shore of West Australia was fading into a blue haze. Early stars specked the sky. The soft breeze sighed in the rigging. The *Catalpa* rocked gently, dug her bow decorously into the swells. The sails bellied.

The men drank in the clear, free air.

Hassett said: "Take a last look at it, lads. There was times I never thought I'd see that damned country from the deck of another ship!"

The *Catalpa* worked slowly to windward under her full set of canvas. The breeze was light from the southeast.

16 . Return Engagement

The *Georgette* crawled up to Victoria Quay in Fremantle, her paddles barely turning over. The black gang in her stokehold was shoveling the last of the coal into her hungry boilers as Captain Grady ordered bow and stern lines made fast and the gangplank overside.

He gave a stiffly correct salute to Water Police Superintendent Stone as that disgruntled individual, after first dismissing the Reservists, stalked ashore. Now maybe the *Georgette* could get about her proper business of carrying the Queen's mail. All this folderol of chasing after those Irishmen fair sickened the captain. Besides, that Yankee skipper, Anthony, had seemed a proper sort of chap. Too bad if he was caught by the likes of Stone.

The dockside was jammed. Crowds had gathered from as far as Perth and Rockingham, waiting in a picnic-like mood all day for the ship's return. One look at the dour countenances of Stone, his officers and the Reservists told the story. "They didn't catch them!"

The word flashed through the throng. It spread from dockside to town. Father McCabe heard it, gratefully, in his study. It flashed over the telegraph wires. Bea Warren heard it in far away Bunbury. In Perth, Walsh and McCarty put their wire-cutters away for keepsakes as the news reached them.

There was open rejoicing among the crowd on the jetty that the police had failed and that the prisoners had made good their escape. The general feeling was that the Irishmen had killed no one, nor committed any vile offense against society.

Superintendent Stone had no sooner arrived at his office than an express messenger arrived with an urgent dispatch from Governor Robinson, directing Stone to report posthaste to the official Marine residence.

Gathered at a large conference table there Stone found the Governor, the Colonial Secretary, the Comptroller General, Superintendent Donan and other high-ranking colonial officials. Stalking in angrily, a few moments in Stone's wake, came Captain Grady of the *Georgette*. A few seconds later, all out of breath, Mr. McCleery, agent for the ship, arrived.

"Gentlemen," the Governor began, "we are here for one purpose. The wheels of activity in this coloney must come to a halt until these Irish scoundrels have been apprehended!" He pounded his fist on the table. "I repeat, there is nothing else that matters. Mr. McCleery, as ship's agent, you are hereby informed that the *Georgette* will remain a warship in the service of Her Majesty the Queen until I give release. Is that clear?"

"Perfectly, sir. But, the mails?"

"The mails can wait. This is a matter of state! Captain Grady!"

"At your command, sir!"

"Your vessel must be coaled immediately. How long will it take to fill her bunkers?"

"I can have her ready to sail by noon tomorrow."

"You will have her ready by midnight tonight. Mr. Donan, I want work parties sent down from the Establishment to take care of this coaling operation. Superintendent Stone, I want your Water Police to refresh themselves and I want them aboard the *Georgette* by ten o'clock this night. I want your company of Reservists again mobilized and aboard at the same hour. I will have a company of infantry under command of Colonel Harvest here from Perth before that hour. He will bring artillery with him.

"The *Georgette* must sail by midnight. She must halt this impudent Yankee whaler. She must recapture these traitors to the Crown! Gentlemen, not only our personal honor but the honor of the Colony and of the Queen herself is at stake." He raised his hand in salute. "Gentlemen! To the Queen, God bless her, and quit yourselves like men!"

Sweating convicts rushed thirty tons of coal into her bunkers. The Water Police and the Reservists, grumbling, were back on board before ten o'clock. Colonel Harvest's company of Infantry arrived from Perth with a twelve-pound fieldpiece which was firmly lashed in the gangway. Powder, round shot and canister were stored beside the cannon.

The *Georgette* beat the deadline by one hour.

Paddle-wheels churning whitely, she headed for the open sea. As she gained headway, her sails were broken out and set to aid her engine.

The crowd, which had gathered at the dock again in early evening when word of the new chase spread around the town, watched silently as the ship faded into the night. There were few who would wager a farthing against a pound that the *Georgette* would fail.

Every muscle in George Anthony's brawny body ached from his thirty-six hours at the twenty-three-foot-long steering oar. He stripped to the waist and had one of the crew rub his back with opedildoc. Then he went on deck. All through the night he stood by the helmsman while the dead-tired crew of the rescuing whale-boat and the equally exhausted passengers slept soundly.

With the first light of dawn Wednesday he was in the maintop with his telescope, scanning the dim horizon for signs of pursuit. It was not in the nature of the bulldog English to give up. He knew the only reason the Water Police cutter had withdrawn yesterday was that her crew was badly outnumbered and her coxswain had realized he could not hope to win a fight. But the English would be back—this time in the *Georgette*.

Breslin emerged from the aft ladder, rubbing the sleep from his tired eyes, and joined the Captain on the weather rail. "You've seen nothing?" he asked hopefully.

"It's too early yet."

"Do you think they'll be at us today?"

"No 'think' about it. They will. This time they'll mean business."

The nightshades drew out to sea. A ruddy glow spread over the distant land. The wind was light, almost like a calm for the heavy whaler.

"Sail ho!" the mainmast lookout yelled.

All thought of pain and weariness vanished for the Captain. "Where away?"

"On th' lee bow, sar!"

"Can you make her out?"

"Not yet, sar!"

First Mate Smith joined them. He swung up to the foremast rings, peered through a glass, then slid rapidly to the deck.

"She's the *Georgette*!" he announced excitedly. "By God, sir, we'll have a fight with them damn Britishers at last!"

The *Georgette* pounded directly for them. Her funnel belched black smoke. All her sails were set but did little to help her in the light air. She steered a course that would put her square across the bow of the wallowing whaler.

The clouds that had been red with sun-up grew heavier. The wind picked up and flecked the gray sea with white. The *Catalpa* heeled a bit, and a twin curl of white water lashed from her heavy bow.

By seven the *Georgette* had come abreast of the *Catalpa*. She shifted course slightly and kept alongside about a mile away.

"She has a man-o'-war flag flying, and a vice admiral's flag too," Captain Anthony reported. "That means she's been commissioned as a war vessel. She's armed, has soldiers aboard and is ready to try to board us."

"If she can!" Sam cut in.

The Captain studied the Englishman again. "Yep, she's got a fieldpiece on her deck. It's lashed at the gangway midships. I can see its muzzle. Steady as you go, helmsman!"

The *Georgette* held to her parallel course. The two ships plowed along, the rising wind now giving the *Catalpa* a slight advantage. The whaler began to inch ahead. For a few minutes the *Georgette* lagged.

"Can't be she's going to quit!" Captain Anthony said incredulously.

But the English ship's paddle-wheels began to churn faster.

"She's changed course," Sam said. "She's comin' fer us!"

The *Georgette* drew up abeam of the bark on a slightly converging course. She still was well to windward, with the evident intention of crowding the *Catalpa* closer to shore. The breeze was getting stronger. Whitecaps frothed the water. Heavy clouds darkened the whole sky. The *Catalpa* now had the wind she liked. She dug her bow into the swells and began once more to draw ahead of the Englishman. Again the *Georgette* dropped astern, until she was more than three quarters of a mile behind and still about a mile to windward. Again the bark's people began to hope the pursuers might give up.

But the *Georgette*'s paddle-wheels cut more hungrily into the waves and she began once more to overhaul the bark.

At a quarter to eight she was so close that the gaudy red, white and gold of the uniforms of the reserves, the regulars and the Water Police could be made out. Bayonets were fixed on muskets. Sabers dangled at the sides of the officers. A dozen telescopes were leveled on the whaler. A longboat hung on davits ready for use by a boarding party.

"Looks like they're spoilin' to fight!" Captain Anthony observed in some satisfaction. "Well, I didn't come halfway 'round the world to show white feather to any Britisher. I think it's about time we showed him we got weapons too. Mr. Breslin, you go below and see that your men are ready and that their revolvers and pistols are loaded. But, for the Lord's sake, keep 'em out of sight. I don't want to give him the satisfaction of being sure your men are aboard. And I want you for a reserve. When I need you, come a fight, I'll yell for you quick enough. Mr. Smith, take a couple of hands below and fetch the rest of our muskets. We got six all told and there's a half dozen revolvers. Pass the weapons on deck. The watch below can have cutting spades and lances."

The First Mate started for the aft ladder.

"And Sam," the Captain added, "bring up that newfangled bomb gun Eben Pierce dreamed up. I never saw fit to use it on sparm—the noise of it would gallie a dead whale—but I hanker to see what she'll do against that vessel yonder."

The deck watch was soon armed with the muskets and revolvers. Sam served fifty rounds of ammunition to each weapon. The bomb gun ammunition consisted of brass explosive cartridges, each fourteen inches long, with time fuses attached.

The captain patted the heavy shoulder gun. "Ugly-lookin' thing, ain't she?" he said. "Cost aplenty. John Wadsworth sold it to me. Said it'd kill a sparm quicker'n any lance. You take it, Sam. Mind it don't knock you clear overside. I'll warrent she kicks worse'n an old goose gun."

The *Georgette* had edged to about a quarter mile abeam. The wind was considerably stronger and swinging more easterly. Both ships were doing about seven knots. The *Catalpa* held a lead of about half a ship's length.

"Sam," Captain Anthony said, "it's about time we showed 'em we mean business too. Call all hands. Get our people on deck." He nodded to Breslin. "Keep your men below yet awhile, Mr. Breslin."

"*All hands! All hands!*" Smith bawled.

The *Catalpa* men scrambled on deck. For those who had the watch below, it was their first sight of the oncoming British ship. They looked at her, bewildered.

"Mr. Smith!" the Captain ordered. "Serve out cutting spades and lances——"

Breslin interrupted. "Captain, with your permission, I'd like to tell them what they're up against. May I speak to your men?"

"Certainly, sir. Men, pay heed to Mr. Breslin here."

Breslin pointed to the Britisher. "That ship there is an English warship. She has a cannon—you can see it plain—and you can see the bayonets on the muskets of the soldiers on her deck. She aims to board this ship and take all of us passengers and all of you crewmen back to shore and clap every last man in prison. You all know the men some of you rowed here to this ship were men who had escaped from the Fremantle prison. Maybe you think the men that were taken off the beach were bad men, that they killed people. Well, they didn't, and your Captain will back me up on that." Anthony nodded. "They were put in prison because they tried to free Ireland from the English.

"I know you all got mad because you've taken so few whales. And some of you called Captain Anthony a hard-luck skipper. This voyage to Australia to rescue these men was his big job. This ship was bought and he was hired to do just that.

"You aren't going to lose a penny because you didn't have luck whaling. I promise you that, at the end of this voyage, each one of you will be paid a lay the equal of whatever the best of the New Bedford fleet has earned in the seasons since the *Catalpa* sailed. And you'll get a whopping bonus too."

He paused to let his words sink in. The crew stood silent. He went on.

"The men over on that ship there—" and he waved his hand toward the *Georgette*—"are ready to fight. If we lose and we are caught, all of us will be thrown into the same prison from which we freed these men. While you are in stone cells there, you will hear the roll of drums that will tell you that us Irishmen have gone to the gallows.

"That ship has sails and she has a steam engine and paddle-wheels. She can rake us with cannon fire. She can shoot our masts out. She can set us afire. But until she does, I propose to fight. My fellow Irishmen will fight. So will Captain Anthony and First Mate Smith—and so, I hope, will you."

He paused again and looked full on the faces of the now muttering men.

"Of course, you can save yourselves by not fighting. You can give up the minute an Englishman steps on this deck. If you surrender, likely you'll only get a few days or weeks in jail. But if you want to back us up, if you want to stand alongside your Captain and your officers—it's up to you. Now, what do you say?"

Breslin folded his arms and waited.

The *Catalpa* men stirred uneasily, looking for a spokesman.

Then Cyrus Hill, bad boy of the voyage, stepped a pace forward. Hill swallowed hard. "With the Cap'n's permit?" He paused for Anthony's short nod. "With the Cap'n's permit then, Mr. Breslin, I reckon you don't know it, but I bin at the bottom of a hull lot o' devilment aboard this here whaleship. I jumped ship and I sounded off 'bout my rights. Mr. Smith here give me a lesson then!" He grinned sheepishly at the First Mate. "Now mind, I ain't takin' back some o' the things I said. I got my rights and I knows it. But it 'pears some folks ain't got some o' the rights I've had all my life. I thought the Cap'n was puttin' it on to me. Now I see what he was aimin' at, mebbe I'm glad he hauled me back."

He squinted his eyes and peered closely at Breslin.

"You say you're goin' to pay us a big bonus at the end o' the voyage, Mr. Breslin?"

Breslin nodded. "That's right."

"And you're going to fight them Britishers?"

"We are that."

Hill turned to the captain. "You going to fight them Britishers too, Cap'n?"

"I am!"

"An' you, Mr. Smith?"

"You're damn right I am."

Hill grinned. "Now them's the best words I ever heard on this ship. I bin itchin' fer a fight fer months now. Guess I had it in me blood. You going to fight—" Hill took a stride towards Breslin—"then, by God, I'm your man. I'm with you, Mr. Breslin, and the crew's with you too!"

Hill stuck out his calloused palm. Breslin grabbed it.

"All right, speechin's over. Mr. Smith," Captain Anthony called, "serve out the spades and lances!"

Aboard the *Georgette*, the fieldpiece had been run out. The gunners stood to their quarters. The Water Police ranged along the rail. Behind them stood the regulars. Back of them were the Reservists.

The wind had blown up to a near gale. White water from the bows of the plunging ships showered decks with spray. The sky was inky black, the sea a mass of froth-capped waves.

The *Georgette*'s master had trumpet to lips. His sailors scurried aloft and took in royals and topgallants.

Captain Anthony grinned. "We got a capful of wind at last, Mr. Smith! Haven't we got a few staysails we could set? I think we could get a mite more out of this bark if we spread all our canvas!"

The *Catalpa*'s men sprang aloft and spread the bark's last rag of sail. The whaler forged ahead under the worn-gray cloud. The bark heeled to her lee scuppers. The great yards creaked and the masts groaned. Now she drew rapidly ahead of the timorous Britisher.

But the Englishman still had his engines. Clots of smoke steamed into the wind. The *Georgette* evened up with the racing bark, drew slowly alongside.

Suddenly Smith yelled: "Duck! He's goin' to shoot!"

On the *Georgette* Colonel Harvest's saber flashed in air. An artilleryman blew his match to flame. The saber came down. The gunner applied his match to the touch-hole of the fieldpiece.

The *Catalpa* people ducked behind the rail.

There was a puff of dirty smoke. A round shot screeched across the bark's bow. The resounding thud of the explosion shattered the air. The cannon ball geysered into the waves, a hundred yards away.

Captain Anthony turned calmly to his white-faced helmsman. "Steady as you go. Pay no heed to him. He couldn't hit a sparm with an oar. Mr. Smith, ready for battle! Mr. Breslin, keep your men below yet awhile. They'll get a bellyful of fighting when the Britisher tries to board."

The *Catalpa*'s men ranged along the weather rail. The six men with the muskets trained them on the *Georgette*. The others gripped their harpoons, lances and cutting spades. Sam readied the bomb gun.

Two anxious minutes crawled by.

The artillerymen ran their piece in, sponged, reloaded smartly and trained again on the whaler. Again the saber flashed high in air. The cannon roared and leaped in its lashings. Another round shot sent water showering over the bark's headsails in a near miss.

The two vessels rolled along, side by side, about two hundred yards apart, the *Georgette* very slightly in the lead. The gunners sponged, reloaded and retrained their piece.

"This time they won't miss!" Anthony warned Breslin. He stepped to the rail and raised his speaking trumpet.

"What do you mean by firing on my ship?" he yelled.

A tall man on the *Georgette* stepped out of the knot of gaudily clad officers on the English ship, speaking trumpet in hand.

Breslin studied the man. "That's Water Police Captain Stone," he said.

"Heave to!" came the command from Stone.

"Why should I?" Anthony demanded.

There was no reply from the *Georgette*.

Captain Anthony raised his voice to an angry shout. "I said, why should I stop for you? I'm on the high seas. What the hell do you mean shooting at me?"

"Have you any convict prisoners aboard?"

Captain Anthony shouted back: "Every man on this vessel is free just like every one in America. You talk nonsense."

"You have convict prisoners aboard!" Stone insisted.

"I tell you we have no convicts on board! Every man is a free man!"

Again Stone hailed: "I give you fifteen minutes to consider. If you don't heave to and surrender those convicts, I'll blow the masts out of you, board you and take you all prisoners."

The *Georgette* started to close in.

Captain Anthony shouted with all the might of his powerful

lungs: "You see that American flag at our peak? That means we are all free men on this ship! If you fire on this ship again, you fire on the American flag! That's an act of war, sir!"

There was no reply from the *Georgette*. The officers on her deck huddled together, talking, waving hands in air. Both ships coursed along side by side, the only noise the roar of the wind, the crash of their bows in the heavy seas, the groaning of masts, spars and cordage and the heavy rumble of the English ship's paddles.

Anthony turned to Breslin. "He'll try to board. We'd best get ready for it. Tell your men that when they hear the first shots they're to hustle up on deck ready to shoot. Mr. Smith, have some of our people break out those spare grindstones from below. And fetch some extra spars too. If he tries to come alongside to board, we'll heave them overboard and smash his boats to bits."

Suddenly the foremast lookout shouted: "Sail ho!"

"Where away?"

"On the lee bow, sar!"

A small boat was coming up between the *Catalpa* and the shore.

"We're getting in too close," Captain Anthony said quietly. "If we don't change course we'll really be in British waters and we'll be in one hell of a mess, without a leg to stand on and maybe a ship to sail on. Sam! Man sheets and tacks. We'll 'bout ship. I think we can scare the white liver out of this Englishman."

Captain Anthony eyed the enemy ship. "Keep her full for stays!" he yelled to his helmsmen. The *Catalpa* men dropped their weapons and manned sheets and braces. The sails held taut in the gale.

"Ready about! Lee—oh! Down helm!"

The helmsman spun the big wheel in the direction of the wind. Working as a perfect machine, the bark's men eased the foresheet and jib sheets to take the weight of the wind out of them. The great yards pivoted about the masts. For a moment there was a tremendous, thunderous shattering of canvas as the wind tore at the sails in their new positions.

"Mainsail—*haul!*"

The *Catalpa*'s sails filled with a roar on the new tack. Her heavy oaken prow, built to crush six feet of Arctic ice, bore down on the larger but more lightly built *Georgette*.

The sudden move on the whaler's part threw the Englishman's complement into utter confusion.

On boiled the whaler, her great bowsprit a gigantic javelin, her bluff bow a monster battering ram.

The line of the Water Police broke in fear. They raced from the rail. The infantrymen joined the stampede to get away from the menacing bark.

Captain Grady, petrified for a moment, leaped into action. "Clear my decks! Get those tin soldiers out of the way! Haul those sails aback! He's going to ram!" He jangled his engine room frantically. "Full ahead port! Full astern starboard!"

The big paddle-wheels churned in opposite directions. Sailors raced for sheets and braces, bowling over the soldiers who got in their way. The sails slatted wildly. The *Georgette* hung for a moment, then, with agonizing slowness, swung in a circle out of the way of the onrushing whaler. The Yankee ship missed the *Georgette* by a matter of inches.

Captain Anthony tipped his cap jauntily to the flustered Captain Grady as the two ships swept apart. Grady shook his head—but touched his cap in salute to the Yankee's audacity.

Cheers went up from the *Catalpa* men. But the English ship, circling full astern, took a commanding spot to rake them. The British officers had their men back in line of battle. The fieldpiece was trained on the bark again. The gunners stood ready.

"Watch lively now, men!" Captain Anthony warned. "If she means to rake us now's her chance. Watch that cannoneer. When his match flares, duck below the rail. Mr. Smith!"

"Aye, Captain?"

"Have some of our men ready with axes to clear away wreckage. Have the others stand by to repel boarders. Mr. Breslin!"

"Ready, Captain!"

"Be alert to warn your men. When the shooting starts, yell

221

for them. That Englishman wants a fight. We'll give him one."

Stone's ultimatum had ticked off minutes before. The *Georgette,* her paddle-wheels slapping the waves at full speed ahead, surged across the *Catalpa*'s white wake, a hundred yards astern. The whaler's helmsman gripped the spokes of his wheel, the knuckles of his bronzed hands dead-white. The Britisher was in perfect position for a shot that would bring the *Catalpa*'s masts and rigging down in a crashing mass.

On the English ship, the artillery officer again poised with his signaling saber.

But the order to fire didn't come. Instead the *Georgette*'s master called on his engine room for more speed, ranged his ship once more alongside the whaler.

Once more Stone trumpeted: "Won't you surrender to our government?" His words were a plea now, instead of an order.

Captain Anthony studied the set of his sails, scornfully refusing reply.

"I see three of those convicts on board your ship right now!" Stone insisted weakly.

"Those are three of my crew!" Anthony answered.

"I demand that you give them up. Heave to!"

"Try and make me. You've got the guns. Come on and fight!" Anthony taunted.

The two ships held parallel courses about two hundred yards apart for another two minutes. Aboard the *Georgette* the English officers huddled in conference.

Again Stone hailed the bark: "Can I come aboard you?"

"No, sir, not you nor any other Britisher on the high seas. I'm bound for home and I won't stop!"

Still the *Georgette* clung to their side. For a half hour the ships thundered along. From the deck of the bark all watched the deliberations taking place on the English ship. Finally, as if shrugging her wet shoulders, the *Georgette* sheared off and set course for Fremantle, her military officers still in an animated huddle, her artillerymen still standing by their piece.

"You can alert your men now, Mr. Breslin!" Captain Anthony said, quietly.

Breslin ran for the companionway. Out of the hold the Fenians tumbled, guns in hand. In the light they blinked, looking for the foe.

"There!" Breslin pointed at the retreating *Georgette*. "There goes the last you'll see of England!"

"Glory be to God!" said Hassett feelingly.

"And an amen to that," Harrington said.

17 . Made Fast

On June 6 the *Catalpa* came almost to Tristan da Cunha in doubling the Cape of Good Hope.

John Boyle O'Reilly sat in his editorial office in Boston that day. A copy boy for *The Pilot* brought him a cablegram. He opened it and read, scarcely believing his eyes at first:

"LONDON, June 6—A dispatch from Melbourne, Australia, states that all the political prisoners confined in Western Australia have escaped on the American whaleship *Catalpa* . . ."

"They made it!" he breathed. Then his voice rose to a shout. "They did it! They escaped!"

Feverishly O'Reilly dipped pen in ink for an addition to the momentous dispatch. His pen spluttered across the paper, his words poured out in a torrent. He closed: "There has never been an enterprise so large and so terribly dangerous carried out more admirably. It will be remembered of Irish patriots that they never forget their suffering brothers. The prisoners who have escaped are humble men, most of them private soldiers. But the PRINCIPLE was at stake—and for this they have been released. England will now realize that she has made a mistake that will follow her to her deathbed in making Ireland so implacable and daring an enemy. . . . The men who sent the *Catalpa* to Australia are just the men to send a hundred *Catalpas* to wipe British commerce from the face of the sea!"

O'Reilly put a triumphant exclamation mark at the end of his article. He called a copy boy. "Hurry! Get me a galley proof as soon as possible."

Devoy must be told. He wrote a message to be sent by telegraph:

To John Devoy
  Editorial Rooms
  New York Herald
  New York, N.Y.
Grand, glorious, complete success. Ireland triumphs. London dispatch admits all our men safe aboard *Catalpa*. Watch your cables from abroad for more details. Erin go bragh. O'Reilly.

Within the hour O'Reilly had ink-wet proofs of his story from the composing room. He stuffed them into his coat pocket, announced he would not be available for the rest of the day, and hurried to the railroad station to take the early afternoon train for New Bedford. He wanted to be first to tell the wife of the Captain of the *Catalpa* about the success of the adventure her heroic husband had undertaken.

Emmie was taking wash from the line while little Sophie toddled after her, putting clothespins into the wicker basket, when the handsome, dark stranger walked into the yard.

Sophie dropped her little handful of pins as she toddled toward him. "Papa?" she asked.

"Ssh, Sophie," Emmie chided. "You know your papa is away out on the sea hunting whales in a great big boat."

O'Reilly picked the little girl up. "I wish I were your papa. He's a hero. The biggest hero in the world!"

Emmie's hand fled to her throat. "You know my husband?" she managed. "Is . . . is there anything wrong . . . Mister . . ."

"Wrong! I should say not. Everything is a thousand per cent right. I am John Boyle O'Reilly. I do know your husband, ma'am. And he is indeed a hero—not only to those of us who know him, but to all Irishmen all over the world and, indeed, to all freedom-loving people all over the globe!"

Emmie looked at him blankly.

"May we go indoors? It will take a deal of telling . . ."

O'Reilly talked for an hour, giving Emmie all the details of the plot, the voyage, and the news of the rescue.

"Thank you, Mr. O'Reilly," Emmie said finally. "I've been on my knees many an hour praying God that He would take care of my George, for my sake and for the sake of my little one. Now I can ask Him for his safe return . . ."

"And I shall join you in those petitions, ma'am," O'Reilly promised solemnly. "He will be back soon. The moment I learn when the *Catalpa* will reach America, I shall be in touch with you by telegraph. The whole world will be awaiting him, I assure you."

The *Catalpa*'s bottom was barnacle-fouled. Great green streamers of seaweed dragged from her hull. The southeast trades shoved her along—a hundred miles one day, fifty miles another, some days as much as two hundred. Always Captain Anthony kept lookouts posted, watching for an enemy sail, fearful that, by some devil's anti-miracle, word could have been flashed to an English warship—at Capetown, Ascension, St. Helena.

In the tropic heat pitch boiled from the deck planks. Awnings made from worn sails gave a doubtful shade for passengers and crew alike.

John Breslin wrote a song. One soft tropic night, as the winds eased the blistering heat of the day just past, he limned it out for the Fenians. Thereafter, on many a night, the words rang out:

"Right across the Indian Ocean, while the tradewind follows fast,
  Speeds our ship with gentle motion, fear and chains behind
    us cast.
Rolling home! Rolling home! Rolling home across the sea,
  Rolling home to bright Columbia; home to friends and liberty.

"Past 'the Line' and now the Dipper hangs glistening in the sky,
  Onward still! In the blue water, see the gulf weeds passing by.
Homeward! Homeward to Columbia, blow you steady breezes,
    blow,
  Till we hear it from the masthead, the joyful cry, 'Land ho!'"

Anthony and Breslin had a conference late one night under the whale-oil lamp in the Captain's cabin. "We can take some whales, Mr. Breslin, if you have a mind," the Captain argued. "It would earn a bit more for the ship—mean more to my men and would take some of the burden off the pocketbooks of your friends in the States."

Breslin frowned. "I'd like to make a profit, of course. If we can go back with the men and a nice cargo of oil to boot, I know the committee would be happy. But the men want to get to America. That's their land of freedom."

So again lookouts manned the rings, scanning the wide seas for telltale spouts.

But once more the *Catalpa* proved a cantankerous, unlucky ship. Light airs plagued her. She fairly crept along. Day followed interminable day. Week dragged after long week, as she slogged westward. Between decks the reek of rancid oil and the stench of bilge became almost unbearable. When they took a whale, the stink of its innards, the blubber fast putrefying in the hot sun, the smudge of oily smoke from the trypots brought howls of anguish from the *Catalpa*'s guests.

The *Catalpa* plodded along, until finally on Friday, August 18, 1876, she neared New York Harbor. At last there was "Land ho!"

There was freedom! There was Columbia! There was America! There was home!

Harrington and Hassett, Hogan, Darragh, Cranston, Wilson leaned against the port rail hungrily straining their eyes for a better view of the land where their dreams would become substance, the land they had never even hoped to see.

The land was low. It made no more than a yellow-edged, dark line on a sullen horizon. As the bark crept closer, the night shadows rolled from the west and down the headlands and into the sea. Only the hoarse chuff-chuff of the towboat's engine and the slap-slap of small waves on the *Catalpa*'s bow broke the stillness.

227

Wilson spoke deliberately. "Ain't much to look at."

Breslin had joined the group. His deep voice commanded silence. "America like that? That's no more America than the tip of my little finger is my whole body. When I left New York for Australia, lads, I traveled the breadth of America. Thousands and thousands of miles wide it is, and thousands from Canada to the south. There's hills and there's mountains and there's tens of millions of acres of land waiting for the men who'll set plow to it. There's cities and towns, and mills and mines and churches and schools and stores. And ships and canals and railroads. You'll find gold all right—if you work for it . . ."

"Aye, work!" Wilson said gloomily. "John, we're old men. Look at us. I'm forty-one. Hassett and Hogan are thirty-eight. Mike Harrington's nearly fifty. Even Bob is thirty-seven and he's the youngest of us jailbirds. Who'll hire such a scrawny lot?"

"You got your two hands, haven't you?" Breslin challenged. "And you have heads on your shoulders! You're Irish, aren't you? Did anyone ever lick an Irishman? Use your hands and your heads. You'll find friendly people who'll be eternally glad you came to help them build what will be the giant of the earth—in your time. Use your hands—use them decently and lawfully. They'll dig up the gold for the——"

"Lace curtains in th' windows!" Cranston sighed.

"Yes, the lace curtains in the windows!" Breslin concluded. "Now get yourselves some sleep. It will be a great day in the morning."

One by one they drifted below. Finally only Breslin remained on deck with the silent members of the watch.

At midnight the *Catalpa* signaled the quarantine ship. The official vessels was ablaze with lights. A dozen small craft— launches, tugs, cutters, sloops, schooners—clustered about her. A small boat shot out from the quarantine ship; the rest of the fleet of small craft surrounding it took off after the small boat. As they neared the bark there was a chorus of shouts: *"Catalpa! Catalpa! Catalpa!"*

The official boat swept alongside. The doctor clambered aboard.

"What goes on here?" Captain Anthony demanded.

"You'll soon find out," the inspector said, grinning mysteriously. "Will you call your hands—and your passengers . . ."

The doctor was brisk and efficient. His examination took but a half hour.

"You may have clearance, Captain," the medical man announced. Then he stepped to the rail, cupped his hands and shouted: "All right, you fellows! Come aboard!"

"Wait!" Captain Anthony objected. "I can't take on passengers here. My towboat is costing my owners money. I can't delay——"

"You won't have to, Captain," the doctor said over his shoulder. "These newspaper people will be glad to have a free ride back to port. Give your towboat captain 'full ahead.' Good-by—and my congratulations on being a hero!"

He swung overside, fighting his way against a human tide of wild-eyed men who swarmed over the rails from port and starboard, bow and stern, yelling: "Breslin! Anthony! Where's th' Fenians? Where's the Captain? Captain! This way . . ."

Over all came a booming voice: "Johnnie! Johnnie Breslin!"

"That's John Devoy!" Breslin yelled.

A black-bearded, black-haired man leaped from the starboard rail and plunged across the deck. He threw his arms about Breslin.

"Johnnie! You did it! The saints be praised! Welcome home!"

Breslin sputtered: "John . . . How did you know. . . ?"

"How did I know? How did all these newspaper people know! Johnnie, the whole world knows what a hero you are and what a hero your grand Captain is too. These men here represent the press of the world. They're here to get your own story of the rescue."

"But we didn't send any message . . ."

"Fast mail steamers spotted you. Clipper ships sighted you and raced into port to spread the news. The electric telegraph station at Sandy Hook reported you nearing port. Now, enough

of that. Help me fight my way over to those brave lads you rescued—m' own lads—th' patient lads I swore in myself!"

Devoy, standing on an up-ended line tub, shouted some semblance of order into the mob scene. Again and again the newspapermen clamored for more about the adventure. Anthony,
Breslin, the Fenians, the crew were hoarse from answering the
thousands of questions. Reporters were still scribbling furiously
as the *Catalpa* dropped anchor off the Battery in New York's
harbor. It was half past one, Saturday morning, August 19, 1876.

The newspapermen boarded their chartered small boats that
had trailed the bark to anchor. Anthony pushed his hair back
from a streaming forehead as the last one went overside. "I don't
think you need be in any rush to report your arrival," he said
drily to Breslin.

By early morning small boats surrounded the bark, full of
curiosity seekers who had read the morning newspaper accounts
and were eager to see the valiant whaleship at close quarters.
Sam Smith had armed guards at the rails to keep any from coming overside.

Anthony called the rescued men together. "Men," he said
simply, "I have secured official permission for you to go ashore.
I'm sorry to lose you as passengers. I have greatly enjoyed your
company, even though we've had our quarrels. I hope the voyage
has been profitable for you." He grinned. "And now you are at
liberty to go ashore when you please."

Darragh took it on himself to be spokesman for all. "Captain,
we're too choked up to say much. But . . . God bless you for
everything. May the road rise before you!"

He shook hands with Anthony. Gravely, each man in turn
clasped the Captain's hand. Then they ducked below for their
dunnage, dropped into a whaleboat—and were gone.

Sunday was a welcome day of rest for Captain and crew. Monday fresh water and fresh victuals were taken aboard. Tuesday
morning early the *Catalpa* weighed anchor. In the late afternoon, Wednesday, she was near New Bedford.

Captain Anthony went below. He donned his best clothes, then ruefully regarded himself. The good blue cloth that had fitted him so well eighteen months ago hung like a sack. He had weighed 163 pounds that long-ago April day. Now he was but a few pounds over 120. He looked in his tiny cabin mirror. The hair that had been dark chestnut was streaked with gray. He shook his head. Well, guess Emmie would recognize him—if she looked hard enough.

He went on deck. The sturdy brick of the whaling capital loomed near. Sam Smith stood at his side. Slowly the bark eased in to City Wharf.

The dock was jammed with a cheering crowd. Hundreds, unable to fight their way on the wharf, massed in the streets shoreward. Police Chief Hathaway struggled to keep them in check.

Familiar faces took shape. There was the olive-tan of John Boyle O'Reilly. There were Father and Mother Richardson. There was star-eyed Amy Chase. And there was Emmie, little Sophie clutching her hand.

There was a lump in George Anthony's throat as he asked: "All lines fast, Mr. Smith?"

"All lines fast, sir!"

"Gangplank secured?"

"Gangplank secured, sir!"

He took Sam's hand. "Good-by, Sam," he said. "Thank you for everything. Never did a captain have a better first officer. Amy Chase is waiting for you. Kiss her for me. Good luck . . . You'll make a grand Captain."

George Smith Anthony took a last look at his ship. She had served him well. Now it was over. She was one of the last of a vanishing line. Steam was replacing sail. Whaling was dying. Kerosene was taking the place of good sperm. Soon the whale would be forgotten.

Now he was through with the sea. Never again would he have to break a vow to the loving wife who waited there for him. Fate had decided. There was a price on his head, just as there was on the Irish patriots he had helped to freedom. The man who had twisted the tail of the British lion could never again put in at one of the Queen's seaports without being arrested instantly.

He squared his shoulders and started down the gangplank. Under his arm was his telescope and the *Catalpa*'s log. On its last page, in a bold hand, were the words: "Went to City Wharf. Made her fast. So ends this day and a pleasant voyage for J. T. Richardson."

Epilogue

The Clan-na-Gael paid off the *Catalpa*'s people as John Breslin had promised. Devoy averaged the whale-oil take of the seven most lucky whalers out of New Bedford in the previous two years. The *Abbott Lawrence* took 312 barrels; the *Charles W. Morgan*, 375; the *Peru*, 600; the *Pioneer*, 700; the *Precedent Second*, 700; the *Sarah B. Hale*, 400; and the *Janet*, 750. The average was 549 barrels. Oil was upwards of a half dollar a gallon. Each barrel measured 31½ gallons. The *Catalpa* herself had taken 310 barrels.

George Anthony shared $2,165.63 of the amount earned directly by his ship. From the average struck off from the seven most successful vessels, his lay amounted to $877.99. The *Catalpa* committee gave him $1,000 in token of their esteem and gratitude. His total reward for the voyage was $4,045.62.

Sam Smith, as First Mate, with a gift of $200 from the committee, received $2,230.41 as his share.

Total cost of the voyage was $25,858.02, according to Devoy's final accounting.

The *Catalpa* was given by the Clan to Captain Anthony and his father-in-law. She sailed April 24, 1877, under Captain Ariel Chase, whaling. On October 27, 1879, she voyaged again under command of Captain E. E. Hammond. Her final voyage out of New Bedford was in 1881. She sailed November 10, that year, under command of Captain John B. Tabor.

The bark passed out of American registry in 1884, when she was "sold foreign." She was altered into a coal barge and ended her career on the beach at Belize, British Honduras, where she was condemned and burned.

Sam Smith did get his master's papers, as George Anthony had predicted. A few months after the return of the *Catalpa*, Sam captained the brig *F. H. Morse* out of New Bedford for an Atlantic voyage. Returning, he signed as first mate of the *Rainbow*, and then the *Peru*. He married Amy Chase in 1883. The blood of a long line of seafarers ran in the Jernegans. So it was only natural that Amy Chase voyaged with her new husband to the Pacific coast where he took the *Napoleon* out of San Francisco. Amy went with him on the cruise.

Amy died in San Francisco, January 7, 1899. In March that same year the bereaved Sam sailed for the Arctic in the schooner *Bonanza*. He was first officer of the steam whaler *Belvedere*, and the captain of the *Orca*. He died in 1909 at the age of sixty-three. His ashes and those of his Amy Chase are buried at Edgartown, on the Vineyard, under white gravestones identical in every way but one—his is graven with an anchor, hers with a lyre, tribute to her love of the piano.

Emmie soon restored the lost forty pounds to George's stocky frame, but she never had to worry about the call of the sea again. The moment the *Catalpa* made fast in New Bedford that hot August day marked the end of his seafaring career.

The Anthony house on Second Street was in the path of commercial development in New Bedford. So George and Emmie put it on the market and, using the proceeds of the sale and some of the money received from the *Catalpa* adventure, bought a brand new home at 14 Bay Street, in a more fashionable section of the whaling capital. There, on January 4, 1884, Emmie gave birth to another daughter, named Ethel. Sophie was nine years old.

For the first five years following the return of the *Catalpa*, George was a hard working member of the New Bedford police department, captained by his friend Hathaway. Then, in 1886, under the presidential administration of Grover Cleveland, Captain Anthony received appointment as boarding officer for the

New Bedford Customs House. This position he held for the rest of his days.

It was a post to his liking, for it put him in touch with fellow mariners once more. He "voyaged" again—but on the two wheels of a bicycle that he rode daily to and from work. Many in New Bedford still remember the chunky, gray-mustached, gray-haired man with the ruddy face, who could be gentle and commanding almost in the same breath.

Always George Anthony was deluged with invitations to speak before gatherings of Irish folks. Again and again, always modestly, he recounted the adventure of the *Catalpa* and her rescue of the Fenians.

As for those thankful men, they were soon assimilated into the virile young bloodstream of America. August 6, 1896, three of them, with Captain Anthony, were honored guests at a huge Clan-na-Gael celebration in Philadelphia's Rising Sun Park.

There were ten thousand gathered there that day. The Philadelphia *Times* said: "The great feature of the day's exercises, and that which attracted the most attention was the introduction of Captain George S. Anthony and the presentation by him to the Clan-na-Gael of the flag which floated from the masthead of the whaling bark *Catalpa* which had on board the political prisoners rescued from the penal settlement of Western Australia, when it was overtaken by a British gunboat. Captain Anthony presented the flag from a temporary platform erected on the grounds. After it had been accepted in behalf of the Clan the scene was one of great enthusiasm. The band played the Star Spangled Banner and the Clan-na-Gael Guards fired two volleys in salute."

Martin Hogan was there. So too were Tom Darragh and Bob Cranston. John Breslin had died only a short time before, but he was represented by his brother Michael. John Devoy was there.

Captain Anthony spoke briefly to the throng: "Twenty years ago you came to me with a request to aid you in restoring to freedom some soldiers of liberty confined in England's penal colony of Western Australia. Your story of their sufferings touched my heart and I pledged my word as an American sailor to aid in the good work to the best of my ability.

"The flag which floated over the *Catalpa* on that April day in 1876—the Stars and Stripes which protected the liberated men and their rescuers—I have preserved and cherished for twenty years as a sacred relic. I would fain keep it and hand it down to my children as a family heirloom, but I am confident it will be safe in the keeping of those who were associated with me in an enterprise of which we all have reason to be proud. Your countrymen have always been loyal to the flag of the United States and ever ready to shed their blood for its defense. I, therefore, present you with this flag of the *Catalpa* as a memento of our common share in a good work well done and a token of the sympathy of all true Americans with the cause of liberty in Ireland. I know you will cherish it as I do, and that if the interests of that flag should ever again demand it, your countrymen will be among the first to rally to its defense."

John Devoy accepted the flag for the Clan, saying: "I accept it with pride as a memento of a noble deed and I promise you it shall be cherished by us while life is left us.

"It is the flag of our adopted country under which Irishmen have fought side by side with native Americans on every battlefield where the interests and the honor of that flag were at stake, from Bunker Hill to Appomattox. It is the flag which symbolizes the highest development of human liberty on this earth. . . . The battle of human freedom has not yet been won and the combination of which you formed such an important part may serve as an example worthy of imitation and enlargement in the future. . . . You bore yourself proudly and gallantly like a true American sailor, and you placed the Irish people under heavy obligations to you. . . . Many of those who took part in the rescue and three of the men to whom you helped give liberty are here to do you honor and thank you in the name of the Irish race for the gallant feat you accomplished nineteen years ago, and for your generous gift of this historic flag. . . . Captain Anthony, in the name of the

Clan-na-Gael, I thank you for the *Catalpa*'s flag and wish you a long and happy life."

Captain Anthony had seventeen more years to fulfill that wish. He died in New Bedford, May 22, 1913, lacking just three months and one day of his alloted three score and ten.

His Emmie lived on for many years, finally joining him in the quiet of the churchyard November 5, 1935, at the age of eighty.

BIBLIOGRAPHY

Anthony, Joseph Russell. *Life in New Bedford a Hundred Years Ago.*
The diary of Joseph R. Anthony edited by Zephaniah W. Pease.
New Bedford, Massachusetts: Old Dartmouth Historical Society,
1922.

Casey, John Keegan. *The Rising of the Moon.* Glasgow: Cameron &
Ferguson, 1869.

Devoy, John. *Recollections of an Irish Rebel.* New York: Charles P.
Young Co., 1929.

Diamond, Arthur J. *Fremantle, the Golden Gate of Australia.* Bristol,
England: E. S. & A. Robinson, 1901.

Log of the Bark *Catalpa*

Lord, Robert H.; Sexton, John E. and Harrington, Edward T. *History
of the Archdiocese of Boston in the Various Stages of its Development.* New York: Sheed & Ward, 1944.

MacManus, Seumas. *The Story of the Irish Race.* New York: The Irish
Publishing Co., 1921. Subscriber's edition.

Mason, Redfern. *The Song Lore of Ireland.* New York: Wessels &
Bissell Co., 1910.

O'Reilly, John Boyle. *Moondyne: A story of convict life in Australia.*
London: G. Routledge & Sons, 188?.

Pease, Zephaniah W. *The Catalpa Expedition.* New Bedford, Massachusetts: G. S. Anthony, 1897.

Roche, James Jeffrey. *Life of John Boyle O'Reilly, Together with his
complete poems and speeches, edited by Mrs. John Boyle O'Reilly.*
New York: Cassell Publishing Co., 1891.

Schofield, William Greenough. *Seek for a Hero; The story of John
Boyle O'Reilly.* New York: Kenedy, © 1956.

Villiers, Alan. *The Way of a Ship.* New York: Scribner, 1953.